The Healers

THE HEALERS

BY
Anonymous, M.D.

G. P. Putnam's Sons   New York

Copyright © 1967 by G. P. Putnam's Sons

Contents

First Questions   9
A Personal Note   13
How It Begins   23
Perfecting a Practice   26
The Numbers   35
Only One Mistake   38
The Long Shortage   42
Where the Doctors Are   53
George Won't Do It   55
A Fee Grows in Brooklyn   60
Dr. Sincere   66
Diagnosis: Blue Cross   75
Doctor Without Patients   81
Anatomy of a Private Hospital   91
Dr. Jekyll and Dr. Hyde   108
My Own Personal, Private Doctor   116
Skin Game   121
Bad Blood   127
Money Matters   132
You Ought to Be Ashamed, Doctor   138
Burckhardt   145
The Discount Doctor   164
The Economics of Abortion   175
Prejudice   186

5

CONTENTS 6

The A.M.A.—Profile in Greed   195
Second Thoughts on Medicare   204
Thinking About the Unthinkable   206
Magicians and Monsters   213
The Good Guys   223
Good Medicine—A View of the Future   229
The Shape of Things to Come   237
Index   245

Whatsoever things I see or hear concerning the life of men, in my attendance on the sick or even apart therefrom, which ought not to be noised abroad, I will keep silence thereon, counting such things to be as sacred secrets.

—from the oath attributed to Hippocrates of Cos, *circa* 400 B.C.

First Questions

It was 3:19 of a cold January morning. I was a green young resident, age twenty-nine, and I was fast asleep. As hospital beds went, this one wasn't bad. You don't pay too much attention to how good a bed is when you're in residency because you really don't spend too many long stretches lying in it.

"Doctor?" It was the night nurse on the maternity floor. "Doctor Hagen's patient is in labor."

"Yes?"

"She's ready for delivery and Doctor Hagen is here."

"Good. Thanks. Good night." I hung up and went back to sleep. Or almost. It took the maternity nurse less than a minute to realize I hadn't been fully roused. Off went the bell again.

"Yes?" This time I was irritated and I showed it. You don't harass residents in this fashion. While not yet truly God-like, residents get a fairly full measure of respect, especially from nurses.

"I don't believe you heard me, Doctor. I said Doctor Hagen's patient was ready and—"

"And I said 'good night,' " I snapped.

At the other end of the phone there was a vague rumbling noise. Then, without warning, I heard a different voice, deep, masterful, penetrating even my sleep-clogged brain, the voice of an "attending" physician, a superior who could make or break me, the voice of Hagen himself.

9

"Doctor," he announced, "on Hagen's time you don't sleep."

"Yes, Doctor Hagen."

"The lady is fully dilated, caput is showing and I want you up here on the double." Click.

At 3:22, more or less fully clothed and reasonably wide-awake, I dashed into the maternity wing, still buttoning my jacket. Hagen smiled benignly up at me. He was a thin little man, hardly more than an inch or two over five feet. He affected elevator shoes, pinstripe suits, a waxed moustache, red satin vest, spats and a fresh cornflower in his lapel.

At this hour of the morning, Hagen and his cornflower were the only fresh things in sight. He crossed his legs with their razor-sharp trouser creases, lit a small cigar, leaned back on a chair in the doctors' room and began filling out the Board of Health birth form, employing for this purpose a rather ornate mother-of-pearl fountain pen.

"The patient," he remarked almost as an afterthought, "is waiting."

Twenty minutes later it was all over. The birth was perfectly normal and both mother and child were doing well. This child, a husky boy, is probably getting out of college about now. One day he may even be President of the United States.

I made my way back to the doctors' room where Hagen, moustache undaunted, spats spotless, cornflower vibrant, was posed thoughtfully over the Board of Health form.

"A boy. Seven pounds, nine ounces."

Hagen nodded with satisfaction, completed the empty spaces on the form, signed his name with a very natty flourish and then, as if this were a film suddenly speeded up, hopped to his feet and began running.

Like a dervish possessed, Hagen whirled through the room, doffing his jacket, cramming a white cap on his head and flinging a red satin vest on a chair. Then he put on a "scrub suit," gown and surgical gloves.

Now, by God, he looked like a doctor, especially when he pulled the surgical mask up over his waxed moustache. Still moving like an old-time movie, he dashed into the delivery room where they were cleaning away the afterbirth. "Hold it!" Hagen yelped.

Working with utmost speed but great artistry, he scooped up a double handful of placenta and blood and smeared himself generously from cap to hem. Now, by God, he not only looked like a doctor, he even resembled a working one.

Suddenly, slow motion set in. Hagen began the weary trudge to the fathers' waiting room. At this hour only two men were sitting there but the air was thickly blue with cigarette smoke. Hagen paused ominously in the doorway and clawed the bloody mask from his face. You could tell this was a crisis: his moustache was awry. Slowly he pulled off the gloves.

Across the smoke, a man jumped to his feet, a comic-strip caricature, tie askew, cheeks blue, surrounded by loaded ashtrays. The husband's mouth worked soundlessly. He took a staggering step across the room.

"I ... y-you ... what ..." His voice gave out.

With one hand behind him, Hagen pressed against my chest in an unmistakable get-lost gesture. With the other hand outstretched toward the miserable wretch, Hagen moved slowly, wearily forward, blood and tissue gory across his gown. He reached the father barely in time to keep him from collapsing in a heap.

"Doctor," the man pleaded, "what ..."

Hagen prodded the man with his finger. "You ... are a very ... lucky man." His voice was tired but firm. "Not only," prod, "did I save ... the mother," prod-prod, "but ... I managed ... to save the baby, too."

First questions to ask?

Many.

But before that, a kind of answer. Charlatan though he was, con man, master psychologist playing on the emotions of patients and their families, Hagen was nevertheless an honest quack.

Unlike some charlatans, he had the good sense to use other doctors and thus keep his patients' death rate low. If you were under Hagen's care you could end up thousands of dollars in debt, but at least you were alive.

With any luck you could even grow up to be President of the United States.

A Personal Note

It may seem strange that a doctor in his middle years, having spent the greater part of his life in training and practice, suddenly does what I propose to do in this book. Questions arise. If I really feel this way about the medicine being practiced and about some of my fellow practitioners, why have I waited so long to speak? Why have I stood silently by all these years? What can I hope to gain by speaking now?

Let me begin, therefore, with this personal note. It may help explain why I am doing this and why it has taken me some years to reach the point where I can do it.

For reasons that will soon become obvious, I cannot fully identify myself in these pages, but there are certain things you will find useful to know. I am a gynecologist-obstetrician. I was born in Chicago, trained here and in New York and now work here. Although I have frequently visited other cities to study and to work, the vast bulk of my experience has been in Chicago and New York.

I am, of course, an M.D., licensed to practice in several states. I am a diplomate of the American Boards of Obstetrics and Gynecology and a fellow of both the American College of Surgeons and the American College of Obstetricians and Gynecologists.

In addition, I hold these posts: attending physician at a large public hospital; attending physician at a major voluntary hospital; associate clinical professor of obstetrics at a leading medical college here in Chicago and senior attending

13

physician of a team of doctors that covers obstetrical and gynecological service in the voluntary and public hospitals with which I am connected. I head a research committee at the hospital involved in work on a particular aspect of gynecological inquiry and I also serve on the hospital's tissue committee. You will get to know more about some of these various teams, hospitals, committees and the like as we get further into the matter.

These are non-paying jobs. My income is derived mainly from private practice. I have an office in Hyde Park and schedule four office hours three times a week. I also perform surgery.

Obviously there are other Chicago physicians whom these details describe. To become much more specific about my present life and activities would be to reveal more than I am prepared to have known. There is no security problem, however, about my earlier years.

I was born on the South Side immediately prior to World War I and I attended public elementary and high schools in several areas of the city. My parents moved frequently in those early days and the four children—I have a brother and two sisters—tagged along from school to school, always the "new kids," but always able to rely on each other's companionship. That was the era, you recall, now memorialized in our folklore by a few carefree symbols—hip flasks, Stutz bearcats and flappers. I remember the period somewhat differently.

My father was what you would be forced to call an itinerant pharmacist, but a steadfast one. He was steadfast, that is, in refusing to settle down and buy into a drugstore, preferring instead the free life of the open road as he moved casually from pharmacy to pharmacy throughout most of Chicago. One might be tempted to characterize a childhood with such a father as chaotic, insecure and dangerously bruising to the tender psyche of the young. It was not.

It was, instead, a childhood in which, whether I had a cent

in my knickers or not, my credit was good at the neighborhood drugstore for a Green River soda or one of those new concoctions, a sundae. This conferred tremendous status on me among my peers, all of whom understood what was and what wasn't important in life.

When I graduated high school in 1930, drugstores were closing down all over Chicago. My father took the occasion to point out the wisdom of not owning a store; in a depression you had nothing to lose. True, you lost your job, but this could happen to you in good times, too, couldn't it? Just about that time he found work in a small manufacturing chemist's factory in Blue Island and the whole family trooped out into the green suburbs.

Beyond telling you that I earned my Bachelor of Science degree at Illinois and my M.D. at a university medical center that included a major voluntary hospital, the rest of my personal life can remain somewhat hazy. I stopped smoking cigarettes eight years ago, still miss them very much and occasionally have vivid dreams in which I light one and take a long, satisfying drag.

Let me become a bit more personal now and talk about motives.

I believe—whatever the evidence to the contrary—that not every doctor in my generation originally chose medicine solely for the money he would earn. Few professions looked terribly promising during the depression era although, as a job, medicine promised security, if nothing else. But I believe many of us originally chose medicine out of an altruistic desire to help people.

Try to recall the climate of the times; the 1930's were a period of social change, capped by a terrible worldwide struggle against fascism. I believe that some of us who became doctors in that period felt a certain sense of dedication to higher goals. Obviously most of us went far astray. If I have any poignant sense of regret, perhaps it's for that lost honor, if nothing else.

In any event, and for many reasons, you will not find in me any breathless sense of the wonder of the healing art, nor am I given to ponderous rhapsodies on the emotional satisfaction of saving someone's life. It is very satisfying indeed to use your skill to pull a patient through. Nothing can take the place of that feeling. Having said it, consider it said.

Obviously, doctors are not Boy Scouts, nor are they deepdyed dastardly villains. We are merely men living in a system of man's creation that tends to give rather disastrously free license to each of us to fulfill our own needs—or greeds—regardless of the cost to others. In this the doctor is no less guilty than many of his patients.

As you can see, I am not a crusader. I do not believe, for example, that the terrifying abuses I see can necessarily be wiped out. We will have to continue living with many of the things that are radically wrong with medicine because they are also wrong, in some degree, with every other part of the way we live.

In that sense, then, I may perhaps be so battle-scarred a veteran of these wars as to sue for a negotiated peace rather than demand unconditional surrender. Familiarity breeds a certain cynical contempt, but rarely an all-destroying sense of outrage. I plead guilty to lack of faith in the perfectibility of man. We will have to take him as we find him and cope, just cope.

And now, as the commercials put it, a few words about original sin.

If there is any single underlying element to which we can attribute much or all of the corruption in medicine today it is that most of it is practiced for money.

A terribly naïve, terribly simplistic idea, true enough. But if there is an original sin from which the abuses ultimately stem, it is the profit motive in medicine. My intent, obviously, is to illustrate the many ways in which the necessity or desire to make a profit by healing the sick eats away at the integrity, the morality and the honor of a profession and a man.

You will find that this thread of corruption appears in many places and in many guises. It sometimes is flaunted boldly. More often it is a secret sin. Most frequently it is very deliberately disguised as a normal fact of life. Occasionally it produces a genuinely comic situation. The result, at other times, is tragedy. There is no one way it shows its face. The only unifying element is that corruption can be traced to the making of a profit out of sickness and death.

Can this be universally true? Aren't there cases in which a doctor provides honest, competent service and charges a reasonable fee for it? The answer, of course, is yes. A great many doctors try valiantly to remain honest. Some of them succeed.

Another question. Does money really corrupt medicine any more than, say, it corrupts law or politics or religion or education? Answer: no. The making of a profit out of the practice of any profession or calling tends to corrupt that practice. Doctors are not alone in being corruption-prone. Your newspaper's headlines will daily confirm that fact for you. But, as you will learn, doctors are in a singularly strategic position to practice corruption with tremendous success.

A third question. Isn't this primarily just a big-city story? I practice in one. My hospital affiliations are here. Most of the doctors I have known—whom you will come to know in these pages—are here or in New York or San Francisco.

Yes, my locale is the big city. But as bad as things may be here, they are worse elsewhere.

The abuses I find in Chicago and New York, the charlatans with whom I work, the corruption I witness, the needless horrors, the unnecessary anxieties, the useless expenses, the ineptness, the carelessness, the greed . . . these are to be found in every city and town, more likely than not to an even greater extent than in the big ones.

If anything, the big city is a patient's town, a buyer's market in medical care, with a very high doctor-to-patient ratio and a tradition, among middle-class patients at least, of calling for an independent medical opinion in every case from calluses to cancer.

Unlike the street gangs who divide a city into "turfs," doctors cannot carve a New York or Chicago into individual holdings. Those towns are just too big, too complex and too overcrowded for that. The place for that, obviously, is the smaller city, the Dayton, the Phoenix or Spokane, the Springfield or Ft. Worth or Sioux Falls. This is not, therefore, just a big-city story.

But the problem in smaller cities, towns and villages cuts much deeper than the fundamental corruption. The problem strikes to the core of knowledge a doctor must possess in order to function most effectively in the best interests of his patients.

This fund of knowledge is available in New York, Boston, Chicago, Los Angeles and similarly large, complex urban centers. Through leading hospitals, medical schools and centers, the average doctor in these cities can find the information he must have to keep up with his profession.

Reading the journals—assuming most doctors have the time and inclination for it, which they do not—only skims the surface of the new knowledge daily developing in medicine. Reading the journals, attending the seminars and lectures, participating in the conferences, taking the classes and workshops, all this added to a regular schedule of clinical work in a bona fide hospital . . . these activities keep a doctor familiar with the ongoing rush of new information about his own field of work in medicine.

For the doctor outside a major U. S. city, most of this is simply impossible. He will not make regular, costly pilgrimages in search of knowledge. His patients need him. His family needs his earnings. Besides, he's doing fine on the half-remembered, out-of-date information of twenty years ago, isn't he?

But questions remain unanswered still.

Why have I waited so long to speak? What do I hope, now, to gain by this? Let me answer the first question by suggesting that, despite the sensational matters to which a doctor may become privy, few of us are really so-called men of the world. Ours is a closed-in existence: eight years of academic training and four or five more in hospitals. Our early lives are shuttered by institution walls, books, laboratories, the faces of colleagues and of an army of sick people.

Let me be charitable to my colleagues and, especially, to myself. Let me say that the cloistered existence of the doctor until well into his thirties makes him a late arrival in the Game of Life.

Arriving late, of course, is no excuse either for being blind to the game or for avoiding any value judgments on it. But it does help explain, in part, why it can take a doctor so long to understand how corruption has eaten away at his profession and turned him from a healer of men to one who flourishes on the frightened, the diseased and the dying.

Inevitably, however, there comes a day when he understands, slowly at first, then more fully. But by then he has given too many hostages. He is no longer that pure entity, a doctor. He has become an impure mixture of husband, father, colleague and doctor whose responsibilities to others, whose commitments and promises have begun to outweigh the pure considerations of the healing science.

I am now at that part of my life, fortunately, when many of the commitments have been fulfilled. The children are adults. They have their own lives and livelihoods. Family requirements, by that odd cyclical quality of life, are now as simple as when first we married. Within a year or two, I will give up the last of my private practice and work full time at the medical school where I now serve. And this provides an opportunity, after many years, to speak.

What do I hope to gain? I'm not sure any of us will gain anything immediately. The conditions of which I will speak are of long standing. They represent, as I believe, accurate reflections of the fact that the way we live makes it possible to profit from illness and grow rich on despair. This cannot continue.

Obviously it will not be swept away tomorrow. But it must change. Some of it is already undergoing change, as I hope to explain to you later. We live in a time, like the 1930's, when change, as the song puts it, is "blowin' in the wind."

I have chosen to tell you this story mainly as anecdotes, more or less as things happened to me, in the hope that this will make it easier to see how matters stand and how, perhaps, you can change them. Certainly, you will be better able to put yourself in the position of those who are caught up in this situation.

You may even, some day, find it possible to forgive them.

I shall keep pure and holy, both in my life and in my art.

—from the Oath
of Hippocrates

How It Begins

What makes a Hagen? What makes the tens of thousands of Hagens now practicing in the United States? And what makes the many other doctors beside whom Hagen is a selfless, idealistic angel of mercy?

The process of corruption is fairly well known. There is no real mystery among doctors as to how and where it begins, any more than lawyers, merchants, or Indian chiefs are puzzled by the process of corruption in their own profession, craft or art.

As a matter of fact, so closely do we all live with corruption that it becomes almost too dangerously easy for any one of us to understand how it takes hold and flourishes. It's an old, familiar story and by now, perhaps, even a bit corny.

To understand how it happens to a doctor, retrace his steps to the time when he graduated with his Bachelor's degree. If he's been farsighted enough—and today students know what they want to "be" by the time they leave Sixth Grade or suffer the consequences of indecision—he's taken what is sometimes known as a pre-med program.

Now he devotes four more years to earning his M.D. and a year to an internship, during which he takes his state exams. On the day he passes he can go out into the world and practice medicine. He is known as a General Practitioner. All too many of the G.P.'s currently treating millions of Americans have literally nothing but these five years of medical training to justify their treatment of the sick and dying.

Isn't five years enough? Later we will see that in a very

good medical school a really able student can absorb a great deal of knowledge. What about the mediocre medical school? The average student? What about the poor school and the incompetent student? The initials M.D. after a man's name do not stand for how much he has learned. They mean only that he can legally practice medicine. And they do not guarantee how well he does it.

But the conscientious student who has just won his M.D. knows enough to know that he knows very little. He understands, with the burning idealism of the twenty-six-year-old who has spent the last nine years cloistered in college, that he is only just beginning to know medicine. He realizes that he needs a great deal of practical experience to back up his theoretical training. And, perhaps most important, he begins to appreciate the fact that medicine is not a fixed body of knowledge, any more than nuclear physics or any other science. He comes to know that everything mankind has learned of medicine from the dawn of history until, perhaps, the year 1920, is equal in volume to the knowledge it has gained in the mere forty-odd years since then.

Practice medicine after only five years of training? Legally condoned, morally wrong. So the conscientious student, having picked out an area of specialization, goes into resident training in that field.

If one had to place a small yellow dot next to the point where corruption can first lay hands on the fledgling doctor, it is here, at the moment when he has his M.D. and he decides what his next step shall be.

Now the pressures of society make themselves felt in a very real way. Yes, the new doctor may have waited on tables to work his way through medical school. He may already have a very poignant understanding of the pressures of society. But from here on in, those pressures begin to mount until eventually, within one to five years, the doctor emerges the way a casting leaves a mold ... whole or flawed.

The dialogue is pure soap opera: "Son, you've got your M.D. Don't you think it's time you paid back your dad for your med-school tuition? Must you keep on going to school?"

Or else it's Edward Albee: "I'm tired of working in that stinking office while you bury your nose in books. I want to live, buy clothes, have a better apartment. I want children, a summer place, a car. I'm sick of being married to a perennial student."

Or it's impure Mickey Spillane: "A very intimate little resort, see? All we want is a nice-looking young M.D. who can write prescriptions, see?"

If he withstands these and other, subtler pressures, the young doctor who chooses residency has even stronger pressures to face when he finishes his work and goes into private practice.

Here, instead of a small yellow dot, place a big red one. The pressures that induced weaker, less economically secure men to go into practice immediately on winning their M.D.'s now strike with even more telling effect. Now the doctor goes out into the world to make his way.

True, he can remain behind walls. Many a student has elected to remain permanently in school, either as a teacher, a librarian, a research worker or, perhaps, one of those professional graduate students who seem always to be in pursuit of a new degree. So, too, the doctor. He can refuse to go out into the world. He can, instead, do research, which pays much less than private practice.

Most residents elect to snap the umbilical cord that has linked them so closely, for anywhere from ten to twelve years, with a school and a hospital. They will and they must go into private practice. They have debts to repay, lives to lead, families to support.

"But I have promises to keep," says Robert Frost. "And miles to go before I sleep."

Perfecting a Practice

Someone ought to do a deep study of the professions in America. They can forget the dull years of training and apprenticeship. Instead, they should concentrate on the exciting moment of truth when a doctor, a lawyer, an architect, actually hangs up his shingle and goes into private practice.

Now, we all know certain home truths. They have been fed us almost with our mother's milk—those of us still alive who belong to the breast-fed generation. We know, for example, that there is Always Room at the Top. We know that there is No Substitute for Hard Work and also that there is a Terrible Need for Doctors (Lawyers) (Architects).

Like most of Mother's truths, these are absolutely true. No question. There is a terrible need for doctors. On the guano docks of Antofagasta. Among the wheatfields of Athabasca. All over Alaska.

Here's where they aren't very desperate for doctors: New York, Phoenix, Chicago, Los Angeles, Detroit, Atlanta, Denver, Philadelphia, San Francisco, Seattle ... any place worth living.

But these big cities draw the medical students because decent training can be found mostly in big cities. And once he's trained, the fledgling doctor tends to remain in the same city for his one to five years of residency in whatever specialty he's chosen. Afterwards, you won't find him packing his bags for the long trip home to set up a practice in Squirrel Bait, Arkansas, or Hawg Jowl, Wyoming. Not him. He's gotten used to the bustle, the excitement and above all the money he can make in New York, Chicago, Los Angeles and all those other magic names. Besides, who ever heard of a specialist in Hawg Jowl?

Be he native or adopted son, the doctor who finishes his residency and goes into private practice has the universal problem of the professional: how does he get business?

Whence come his patients? He's not allowed to advertise. Neither can he hire a press agent. After he's sent announcements to every relative in his own and his wife's family unto fourth cousins twice removed, to every human being whose name he can scrounge up out of his memory, to every patient he ever treated during his residency days, to every relative of every friend and co-worker, to his bartender, the usher at his neighborhood movie house, to the cop who gave him a parking ticket last September . . . what then?

Well, then he sits and waits and watches the money go out . . . for office rent, telephone, answering service, nurse-receptionist. Even if he shares these costs with several other doctors, they still amount to a fairly large bite out of what savings he may have. If he's married, any bookie will give you seven-to-five his wife's working. If he's also got children, the same bookie will give you ten-to-one he's deeply in debt.

How does he spend his days? If he's lucky he may job around here or there, helping out at operations as an assistant. This is the same man who in his days as a resident performed the operations. Now he assists, for a few dollars. Or he works in a clinic. A friend may throw him a little insurance-examination business. But, remember, our hero is a specialist. He didn't spend all those years in residency just to do menial jobs any G.P. fresh out of med school can do.

Obviously, he also spends quite a bit of time at the movies, a relaxing and inexpensive way of killing an afternoon. He sits around his old hospital, drinking coffee in the doctor's lounge. He also calls on doctors he knew during his residency days. He lets it be known he's available. For anything. And he waits.

Just where does a specialist get his patients?

The accepted way that accounts for probably 99 percent

of a specialist's patients is referral. General practitioners, family physicians who have the confidence of their patients often for several generations back, recommend a patient to a specialist. This is virtually the only way the specialist can get work.

Let's pause here for some basic arithmetic. In a big city like Chicago or New York, a G.P. charges about $10 for an office visit. Depending on the neighborhood he's in and his clientele, this fee can drop as low as $7.50 or even $5, never lower, or rise to as high as $15. When he makes a house call, his fee ranges from about $10 to $20, depending on time of day or night and treatment indicated. If, as is often the case, he must give an injection during one of these house calls, the cost is added to the basic fee as an extra charge or passed on as a higher fee.

Now let's look at the specialist's charges. A surgeon rarely performs even the most minor operation for less than $100. Fees of between $250 and $500 are common, depending on the degree of urgency, the nature of the operation and the financial condition of the patient. An operation on a well-to-do patient can certainly cost $1,000. None of these fees include hospital expenses, anesthesia, medication, tests, X-rays or any other services which may be necessary before, during or after surgery.

Arithmetic over. Now let's do some algebra. Doctor X is a G.P. Mrs. Y comes to Dr. X with a condition involving some bleeding, some pain. Dr. X diagnoses a growth, sends Mrs. Y to Dr. Z, a gynecologist. Mrs. Y pays Dr. X $10. But, by the time he has finished removing her growth, Dr. Z takes Mrs. Y for $500.

Does this seem altogether fair? Is it, in fact, even remotely American? True, Dr. Z spent a few more years learning to be a specialist and, therefore, is entitled to charge a few more dollars for his services. But what about lovable, trustworthy Dr. X? Just because he's a G.P., can't his wife have a mink of the same hue as Dr. Z's wife? Can't Dr. X send his children to the same good private school attended by Dr. Z's children? Isn't this America and can't the X family have a summer cottage in the same select community as the Z family?

Why, of course. Doctors long ago recognized that if their public scale of fees presented major inequities, private negotiation squared everything. In a word: fee splitting.

Now we know doctors don't split fees. This is quite beyond the pale of professional ethics and behavior. We all know this. We know congressmen and senators live entirely off their salaries. We know building inspectors are a poor but honest lot. Policemen, too. Also insurance adjusters.

Let's turn off the houselights and watch a little playlet. It's untitled because it's a slice of my own life during that black year or two before I began to build a private practice. Curtain up.

ME: (*making my seventh call of the afternoon, to a general practitioner whose work I had handled for the past five years as a resident*) . . . so I've been in private practice a couple of months now and I was wondering whether you, uh, knew about it or not.

HIM: (*deadpan*) Oh, I knew about it, all right.

ME: (*hintingly*) You used to think pretty highly of my work, didn't you?

HIM: Very highly.

ME: (*suavely*) You, uh, ever get many, uh, gynecological cases?

HIM: (*vaguely*) A few now and then. A few.

ME: Who does your OB-GYN for you?

HIM: (*even vaguer*) Oh, you know, some of the guys.

ME: Like who?

HIM: (*belligerently naming one of the clumsier butchers around town*) Oh, Harry Thumbs.

ME: (*horrified*) Harry Thumbs? Are you kidding? (*The Hippocratic Oath forbids us from blowing the whistle on our fellow doctors, but not to a fellow doctor.*)

HIM: (*quickly*) Another call coming in. Nice talking to you 'Bye. (Click.)

It took a few more of these little playlets, differing only slightly in dialogue from one to the other, before I became thoroughly confused. Here I was, bright, young, well trained and knowledgeable in all the latest techniques. But the very G.P.'s who knew this about me were using specialists who were no better than I and in quite a few cases much worse. Why? Was it my inexperience? But I'd just finished five years of hospital work that in sheer experience were the equal of a dozen years of private practice.

It might have taken me years of fumbling if it hadn't been for Jerry Nuccio. Jerry was about ten years my senior, but we'd both trained at the same medical school, a good one, and to Jerry this counted for something. He didn't know me half as well as some of the others I'd been phoning, dropping in on or casually bumping into at the hospital. In fact, Jerry knew very little about me except that we were fellow alumni and I was reputed to be not too bad at my specialty.

"Sure," he responded right away, "I get a handful of OB-GYN cases every month. I usually send them to one or two guys. You want me to refer a few to you?"

"Jerry, you'd be a lifesaver."

He sat there watching me for a moment as we sipped our coffee in the doctors' lounge of the hospital. "I guess I can afford it," he said then.

Misunderstanding, I blurted out: "You won't regret it, Jerry. I'll treat 'em like eggs in a crate."

He shook his head. "I'm not worried about treatment. It's the money this'll cost me."

"I don't understand," I said. And I didn't.

He glanced around him, us. The nearest possible eavesdropper was several yards away. Nevertheless, Jerry's voice dropped to a whisper. "Don't tell me you're not wise to this," he hissed.

"To what?"

Jerry gazed heavenward in exasperation. "You mean I'm the one who has to break the news to you?" He seemed more exasperated at this personal misfortune than at my own stupidity. "Okay. Listen fast because I'm only telling it once. If you quote me, I'll deny it. If you report me, I'll sue you. But if you're smart you'll get that practice of yours going."

What followed was almost anticlimax. It was couched in perfectly innocent terms. Jerry explained, in the most offhand manner imaginable, that the gynecologists to whom he referred cases called him in as a consultant or to assist with any surgery or other hospital work the case might require.

"If they hit the patient for, say, three hundred dollars, they find a way to get me my consultant's or assistant's fee of one hundred dollars—in cash." Jerry thought for a moment. "It isn't always a third, you understand. Sometimes it's a quarter or a fifth of the fee, depending on how much work they actually have to do."

"And how much time you have to spend consulting or assisting," I added with juvenile sarcasm.

Jerry examined my face for signs of an incipient sneer, jeer or smirk. Finding traces of all three, his own face hardened. "You want me to refer you a case a week? Or you want to be a wise guy?"

The Moment of Truth. I thought of unpaid bills. I thought of afternoons wasted in waiting. I thought of patients who needed what I had to give them. I thought of all the other young specialists trying to start a practice. I thought of all the evasive answers from G.P.'s I'd asked for referrals. I think I thought too long. Jerry threw all his cards on the table.

"Listen, kid," Jerry said then, standing up and reaching for his coat, "if you're mad at me, personally, don't be. If it had to be me who broke the news to you, don't hate me,

thank me." He lighted a cigarette. "And remember, kid, once
the word gets around that I'm referring patients to you, you'll
start getting them from Siemewicz and Harper and Jacobson
and Doheny and Mason and Portnoy and Kovacs and . . ."
His cigarette waved furiously in my face.

I held up my hand to stem the flow of this America-the-
Melting-Pot prose. A referral a week from Jerry Nuccio did
not make a practice. But if he was telling the truth about the
change in my status once his friends learned I was one of
them, I would be well on my way to a real practice in only
a few months' time.

It's hard to think of Jerry Nuccio as a fairy godfather. But
with a wave of his cigarette he had, indeed, changed my life.

For some patients, though conscious that their condition is perilous, recover their health simply through their contentment with the goodness of the physician.

—from Precepts
attributed to
Hippocrates

The Numbers

A great deal about modern life can be expressed in numbers. Even life and death can be reduced to the figures in actuarial tables. Medicine, too, has its numbers.

The key ones are easy to remember because they are the same number—three-quarters—or, to be precise, 75 percent. The first significant application of this figure is in relation to general illness. It can be stated this way:

> *Of all the people who go to*
> *see a doctor, more than 75 percent*
> *would get well without any*
> *medical treatment whatsoever.*

This figure does not, of course, include patients with broken bones, gross injuries, or serious organic malfunctions or disorders. These make up the 10 to 25 percent which could not be cured without qualified medical attention.

What about the rest, that vast army comprised of people who feel sick enough to see a doctor? Are they simply not as sick as they feel? Are they victims of minor psychogenic ailments that the passage of time will alleviate? Are they hypochondriacs who mistake the symptoms of a minor infection for something more serious? Are they youngsters or old people under the control of overanxious families? Self-important people who see catastrophe for civilization in the slightest sniffle? Self-indulgent people who derive their greatest satisfaction from catering to their own whims? Treatment-addicts who must have a fuss made over their own well-being?

All these are part of that vast army of the not-really-sick. But many more regiments are filled with anxiety-ridden souls whose fears center around a specific condition. There are the cardiac battalions, including companies devoted to fear of coronaries, platoons intimately involved with angina and arteriosclerosis squadrons. Other battalions carry the cancer banner. Still more march in fear of ulcers, tuberculosis or other stylish killers. In the rear ranks, hiding their colors, are those unhappy multitudes whose secret fears cannot be revealed to the world, but who see in every twinge and blotch the malevolent guilt of syphilis or the shameful state of impotence.

The 75 percent who would get well without treatment—whether or not they were actually sick to begin with—are as variously motivated in this human endeavor as in any other. But one condition is common to all of them: each is the product of a process of thought conditioning that started in a small way with the first pagan priest who ever exorcised a fever by incantations or guaranteed fertility by blood sacrifice. It has grown, through history, into a mass delusion.

The nature of the delusion produced by this brainwashing is difficult to express concisely. It is an emotional state much complicated by each person's own individual circumstances. But stated as simply as possible—with all the dangers inherent in oversimplification—it is that we are helpless to help ourselves. Sickness is the exclusive province of the doctor. He knows all there is to know about it. We are an ignorant lot and all we can do by treating, or neglecting, ourselves is to let a bad situation deteriorate still further.

What we have here, therefore, is a kind of automatic decision-making which bypasses the normal processes of rational thought and substitutes conditioned response. In this respect, the mind of the 75 percent army functions like a rudimentary computer whose memory has been programmed with only a few selective bits of information and only a few ways of linking the bits together.

There is no onus attached to being a member of this army. In all probability you belong to it. I have, on occasion. It is part of human nature, I suppose, that when faced with even the merest hint of certain dark, primordial fears we react in an illogical, routinized manner.

The other significant application of the 75 percent figure is in the area of surgery. It can be expressed in this fashion:

> *Of all the operations performed*
> *in U. S., more than 75 percent are*
> *unnecessary.*

Is this possible? What do I mean by "unnecessary?" Let me state the situation in another way:

> *The overwhelming majority of*
> *patients who submit to some form*
> *of surgery in a hospital or doctor's*
> *office do not require this surgery;*
> *their condition is not improved by*
> *this surgery; in my opinion, they*
> *constitute more than 75 percent of all*
> *instances of surgery.*

Let me explain this more fully, as a doctor and as a practicing surgeon. There are highly principled, extremely knowledgeable surgeons who perform nothing but operations they are absolutely convinced are necessary to alleviate or cure the patient's condition. In most large cities there are a scant handful of such men.

But the majority of surgeons own a set of principles not entirely without blemish. Their knowledge of their work is

not entirely current. They have been too busy—the deadliest
of the doctor's complaints—to keep up with advances in their
profession and their specialty.

If to this is added the terrible pressures on all of us to
accommodate ourselves to the world and acquire its material
trappings of success, we begin to understand why a lot of
operations which do not need to be done are yet, somehow,
done.

But the interrelation between the two 75 percent figures
gives us our clearest insight into the high prevalence of needless surgery.

Obviously the ideal candidate for unnecessary surgery is
someone who not only is healthy, but who doesn't need any
surgery at all in any manner, shape or form. Where to find
such a paragon? The surgeon locates him with unerring accu-
racy by simply reaching out among the more than 75 percent
of patients who don't need medical care, but seek it.

How does the average not-really-sick visitor to his family
doctor—that trusted friend—end up flat on his back staring at
the operating room lights?

The answer, as we will see, is a typical human mixture of
at least two of the seven deadly sins. I refer to sloth, stirred
with greed.

Only One Mistake

Whenever I meet Rosen—about once a month at a conference or seminar—we usually find ourselves after hours at a
bar near the hospital where both of us once trained. Shortly
after the second drink, one of us always remembers our favorite punch line and we collapse in helpless laughter. The

punch line is to a very old joke, but a true one. The line goes this way: "He made only one mistake."

The story began quietly enough one summer a few years after World War II. Rosen had recently married and the first child was on the way. Like all of us he was struggling to put together a practice that would pay for the rent and also for a baby.

"Fred," his wife remarked one day, "my mother's having some sort of, uh, you know, woman's problem. I mean, she's got this terrible pain down in there and—"

"I'll see her after dinner," Rosen cut in. "Have her meet me at my office."

"I already suggested that. But you know Mom. She's embarrassed. After all, a son-in-law, uh, well, examining her, you know, down there."

Rosen nodded. "I'll refer her to a good man. Remind me in the morning."

But, of course, in the morning both of them forgot, and by evening the situation had taken a dramatic turn. Arriving home Rosen found at the dining room not the dinner he expected but his wife and her mother in postures of utter dejection. A ceremony something like a pre-wake was in progress.

"Hi, Mom," Rosen called with fake cheeriness.

"Ooh," his mother-in-law murmured.

Now the tale unfolded. She had gone to a gynecologist in her neighborhood, an older man, a Dr. Harris.

"George Harris?" Rosen asked. "You couldn't pick a better man. We trained at the same hospital. He was ahead of me, but he'd already built quite a rep even then. I hear he's in line to be chief of obstetrics soon."

This was all well and good, but the news Harris had given Rosen's mother-in-law was not. "Bad?" Rosen asked.

"The worst," his wife intoned.

"Here," his wife's mother said, pushing across the table a sheet of paper. On it Harris had had mimeographed a simplified drawing of the vagina, cervix, uterus, tubes and ovaries. In a number of places, Rosen saw, he had drawn small X's with a bright red pencil.

"The X's?" he asked.

His mother-in-law clasped a palm to her cheek and rocked her head from side to side. "Don't ask. Fibroids."

Rosen frowned and reexamined the drawing. He knew the sheet of paper well. He and Harris had both studied under the same professor, who had developed this chart of the female reproductive system as a teaching aid. Over the years, Rosen and Harris had both sketched on such charts their findings after examining a patient. Now Harris had adopted the drawing for use with his patients.

"There are fourteen of them," Rosen said. "Are you sure?"

"He's sure," his mother-in-law retorted, "your friend, the expert. Fourteen fibroids. But that isn't all. He says they're nothing to fool with, not when they hurt that much, and he wants to check me into the hospital Monday morning, he's going to take every one of them out."

"Hold it," Rosen commanded. "If anybody takes out those fibroids, it's me, at my hospital, with my associates. All right?"

"I don't know. . . ."

"At my fee," Rosen added as a clincher. He then proceeded, on a Friday night, to call the head anesthetist at his hospital and get him to postpone his weekend a day. He checked his wife's mother into the hospital that evening and scheduled her for 8 A.M. surgery the following morning.

"But before we start cutting," he concluded, "we're going to take a look. Okay, Mom?"

"Fred, I don't . . ."

"Okay, the head gynecologist will look at you. And I'll kind of lean over his shoulder."

Which is more or less what happened. His mother-in-law got up on the examining table and the hospital's chief of gynecology began to pinpoint the 14 fibroids. After a few minutes' examination, he turned to Rosen. "You try," he suggested.

To get right to the point, neither the chief nor Rosen could find Fibroid One, let alone Two through Fourteen. They consulted Harris' drawing with its little red X's, but to no avail. All they did find was an exceedingly angry-looking boil, ready to pop, which was apparently causing the pain.

From here on in, Rosen realized, only applied psychology would win the day. "Mom," he said, "we've decided to delay the operation a few days. We can't get the right anesthetist and, anyway, there isn't that much of a rush. But, meanwhile, you've got to cooperate."

"Anything."

"I'm checking you out of the hospital. Go home and get in a hot bath, as hot as you can stand. Call me if anything happens."

"Like what?"

"Like anything."

The call came two hours later. "Such a thing," Rosen's mother-in-law reported to her daughter, still not willing to entrust these matters to Rosen. "A discharge like you can't imagine and all of a sudden the pain is gone. Absolutely, completely gone."

"Tell her it won't be back," Rosen said. "Tell her there won't be any operation. Tell her Harris made only one mistake."

"One? You must mean fourteen."

"Only one mistake."

"What was that?" his wife asked.

"He didn't know she was my mother-in-law."

The Long Shortage

Of every thousand American babies born alive, 25 die before they are a year old.

In countries like the Netherlands or Sweden, of every thousand live births, 15 die within a year.

According to the American Medical Association this is a negligible difference, merely one percentage point. That's true, of course. If the U. S. loses babies at a percentage of 2.5 and the Dutch at 1.5 there is a difference of 1 percent.

That difference is 40,000 American babies a year.

Why? Not because our obstetricians and pediatricians are stupid or badly trained, nor because the European doctors are the possessors of some secret. The fact is that, of the countries of the world which make reliable figures available to the United Nations' statisticians, fourteen nations have an infant-death rate lower than ours.

Well, maybe it's because our women don't produce as healthy babies. Maybe there's something in the polluted air, the pesticide-covered fruit and vegetables, the crowded cities, the sewage-ridden water, the lurking danger of our rising crime rate, the lack of physical exercise because more gadgets do the work—you name it, maybe it affects our women's ability to bear healthy children.

Maybe the tremendous amount of patent medicine consumed in this country is affecting infant mortality. The no-prescription drugs that dry up stuffed noses, the wake-up pills, the relaxation pills, the headache remedies, the cough syrups, the tension reducers—maybe these have an effect. Could it be the prescription drugs, the tranquilizers and sleeping pills and appetite-reducing pills? Could it be the nostrums for tired blood, lazy bowels, bad breath, sweat?

Probably not.

Some very extensive study may yet be made to determine the bad effects of this slough of drugs Americans wallow in, but you and I won't live to see the results.

Until that particular Judgment Day, however, it's the opinion of most honest medical men that the richest country in the world has such a high infant-death rate because there aren't enough doctors to take care of things properly. And the infant-death rate symbolizes a great many other areas in which the U. S. has fallen behind.

The doctor shortage in this country is getting longer by the day. The fastest way to summarize the shortage is to report that, at the moment, U. S. hospitals need 14,000 new doctors a year and U. S. medical schools graduate only 7,000.

If the current lag between population growth and doctor education continues to widen, as it has, with general population expanding at a much faster rate than doctor population, instead of producing only half as many doctors as we need, we soon may produce only a third as many, or a fifth or a tenth.

As I've said, this is a shortage of long standing. Reversing the trend cannot be done overnight. It takes twenty years from kindergarten through medical school to produce one M.D. and two to five years more to make him a specialist. If we started reversing the trend tomorrow morning, in the two to three decades it would take us, the gap would have widened still farther.

But let's get back to those babies again and see if we're right in assuming that the shortage of doctors is mainly responsible for their deaths. Let's begin with the fact that in about 75 percent of all pregnancies, there are no complications. These are the births in which the doctor is a bystander and the mother and the baby do the work, which is as it should be. Of the 25 percent remaining, a lot have relatively minor prenatal problems which simple treatment will cure, or else they produce mechanical complications at birth which the doctor's manipulation can handle.

What remains, and here I am not as sure of my percentages, is a matter of perhaps 5 to 10 percent of all pregnancies in which something serious is wrong or can go wrong. Most of these have received a lot of publicity, and rightly so. They include the Rh factor, the onset of certain diseases like German measles during the first trimeter of pregnancy, heart trouble, narrow pelvis, malpositions, malpresentations and faulty implantation of the placenta.

These 5 to 10 percent of pregnancies which present serious problems require a variety of close attention by a qualified doctor. They require intensive prenatal care. They may require something special in the way of a delivery team. They may also require great vigilance after a successful birth.

All this costs money.

Well-to-do families can afford this kind of attention. Less well-to-do ones may not be able to afford it, but they scrimp and get it anyway. A lot of it can be prepaid through a health insurance plan. But if you have no money and no health insurance you must rely on public hospitals and clinics where the treatment is free.

At this point let me resort to an analogy which is not in the best taste. Let's visualize Main Street after the big I Am an American Day Parade, when all the patriotic groups have marched, the bands have played and the horses—dozens of them—have pranced. Before the street cleaners come along, flights of sparrows get to work. Where there were dozens of horses now there are hundreds of sparrows. This is a fact of life. Two blocks away, on Second Street, only one horse has passed during the day. Second Street collects only a few sparrows. All the action is on Main Street. The smart sparrows flock there.

For Main Street read private practice in private or voluntary hospitals. That's where all the action is, where all the money is to be made by a young doctor. Second Street is the public hospital. You might intern there or even do your residency there. It's a nice place to visit but you wouldn't want to live there. The pay's too low. You didn't devote 20 to 25 years of your life to something that isn't going to pay off big.

Am I saying that pregnant women in public hospitals get worse care than under private attention? If they're having a normal pregnancy, the clinic care is perfectly adequate. But if they're in the risky 5 to 10 percent, public hospital care is usually too little and usually too late.

In a major New England city last year the statisticians broke down the infant-death rate by locale. They found that in neighborhoods of moderate or high income levels, the death rate was about 1.7 percent, which compares favorably with The Netherlands' 1.5. But in areas of low income or no income, the sections of town where welfare funds and public clinic care were keeping most families going, the infant-death rate was closer to 4 percent.

Part of this differential may be due to bad education. Where income is low and education is poor, fewer mothers know about the complications possible during pregnancy, are less adept at spotting signs of trouble and less likely to seek special help. But this is, at best, a quibble. We cannot unload on mothers a responsibility that lies with the medical profession. It is the doctor who has the training to notice and treat complications. But—and this is the crux of the problem—if the doctor is nonexistent because the medical school hasn't produced him, or if he's too overloaded with work to give each case more than a once-over-lightly, the result is a 4 percent infant death rate.

By the way, if you are in any doubt that doctors in public practice are overloaded, let me cite the case of a public hospital in my home town, one of the best hospitals in Chicago or in the entire U. S. It was built to handle 5,000 births a year. It is currently reported to handle in excess of 20,000 a year.

Under such circumstances a public hospital may—as this one does—have some of the best obstetricians in the country. But it's a simple question of too few for too many.

Why are we producing dangerously too few doctors in the richest country in the world, this Great Society dedicated to education and culture and the better life?

For one thing, there aren't enough qualified medical schools, only 89 in the entire country, as opposed to a thousand qualified institutions of higher learning in which one may earn a degree in Chain Store Merchandising, Hotel Management or Scuba Diving.

For another, not enough qualified hospitals are connected with medical schools. Of the more than 7,000 hospitals registered by the American Hospital Association, only a few more than 200 have any meaningful affiliation with a medical school.

For a third thing, the figures begin to look even worse as we move up in medical training from the simple earnings of an M.D. through internships to residencies. As I have said, we currently graduate about 7,000 M.D.'s a year. That was also true ten years ago. That was also true twenty years ago. In fact, you have to go back to before World War II to find a period in which we graduated fewer than 7,000 doctors a year. The growth has been negligible.

Meanwhile, hospitals have been desperate for more doctors. Twenty years ago U. S. hospitals needed about 9,000 new doctors a year as interns. They got 7,000. About 2,000 jobs went begging. Today, as I have said, hospitals need nearly 14,000 new doctors as interns and only 7,000 M.D.'s are produced.

It is true, of course, that since about 1950, hospitals have been accepting graduates of foreign medical schools as interns. Presently about 3,000 M.D.'s from other countries are interning in U. S. hospitals. In actuality, therefore, only 4,000 internships go begging each year. But what about those 3,000 foreign interns? Most of them return to their native lands to practice medicine. While we are happy to have the use of them as interns, we lose their services once their training has ended.

The statistics on resident doctors are, if anything, even gloomier. Twenty years ago U. S. hospitals needed about 9,000 new residents a year and got them, every single one. Ten years ago the picture had already begun to shift out of kilter with 25,000 needed and only 20,000 available, of whom 5,000 were foreign doctors. Today the gaps are spread even wider. Hospitals require about 38,000 residents a year. They get 29,000, of whom about 8,000 are foreign doctors.

How did we get in such a fix?

One of the chief reasons is that, while it was never easy to pay for a medical education, costs have shot so high that fewer families, in relation to the size of the population, can afford to send a son or daughter the whole route.

Most current estimates put the base cost of the four years of graduate work that lead to an M.D. at about $10,000. But this tells us very little. Prior to graduate work come four years of college leading to a Bachelor's degree. This usually costs about $8,000 in tuition, books, fees and the like, but may cost less if the required pre-med program is available at a free state or city college. (It should not need to be pointed out to parents of teen-agers that free colleges do not confer much status and that a free B.S. is worth less than a paid-for one, regardless of the academic standing of the colleges involved.)

So we have a total tuition-books-fees cost of about $18,000 for eight years, plus the expense of living, traveling, wearing clothes, eating, having medical care, which are much less when a youth lives at home and a great deal more when he lives at college. We also have to consider other disheartening facts of life, such as the fact that in a good med school the pace is so ferocious that students have little time or energy with which to take an outside job to help defray expenses.

Moreover, the opportunities for scholarships are much fewer than in other lines of academic endeavor.

Then, too, it costs a college more to train a medical student than any other kind. Colleges estimate that it costs them $75,000 per student. Let's assume this is one of those figures created by accountants that probably include everything but the kitchen sink and which can be altered at will to prove a variety of things the college may want to prove. Even so, it can't be far from the truth. And this particular truth hurts ... all of us.

Who pays for training doctors? Clearly tuition doesn't. The National Institutes of Health make grants to medical colleges, but these are not for tuition. They are earmarked for specific research, and while some of the money gets into the general coffers, most of it must be accounted for by the project being sponsored.

Endowments are the other main source of college income and here the medical school must stand in line with its tin cup held out, just as any other department of the university does. When endowments are given without strings for the university to spend as its needs dictate, the School of Medicine is only one of many that must share. It would take a school administrator with nerves of steel to coolly deploy a large chunk of this endowment money to his dull, workaday medical school by scanting such glamour departments as Physics and Math. The best the med school can hope for is an even break. After all, we need nuclear physicists, too, don't we?

Of course it isn't simply that the infant-death rate can be lowered by educating more doctors. I use this one statistic to stand for all the other problems of U. S. medicine today, many of which can be solved or, at the very least, headed toward solution, by producing more doctors. Yet, as we have seen, it costs the individual doctor—or his family—a minimum of $18,000 in tuition costs alone, while the university says it costs them another $75,000 per student just for graduate work leading to an M.D. To double our present annual rate of 7,000 M.D.'s would cost more than half a billion dollars per year per graduating class.

What money there is, as we have seen, now comes from the student, from government grants and private endowments. In university hospitals, some money is also produced by private-patient service. How much more money can be squeezed from these sources? Obviously the only one not already stretched to its utmost is the government sector.

I am not one who believes the government to be a bottomless money-pit, nor do I lose sight of the fact that "government money" is really the stuff you and I unhappily forked over on April 15th. But it does seem that, as an item for the government to buy, more doctors are easily as worthwhile as more napalm jelly or more thermonuclear devices.

Or am I being naïve? Maybe Malthus was right. Why shouldn't four out of every hundred babies of poor Americans die? Isn't that the natural way to weed out the unfit? Why produce more doctors when our greatest danger is overpopulation? Why not let the supply of doctors continue to fall badly behind?

That way not only will more babies die, but more old people, too. In fact, the poor in every age bracket will, as Malthus suggested, be killed by their own poverty.

I have only one problem with the Malthusian approach. I can never figure out how you administer the thing—whom to let live and whom to let die.

But perhaps the administrators in government and education who have, to date, found no solution to the doctor shortage can turn their talents, instead, to this problem. They may have more success with it.

Healing is a matter of time, but it is sometimes a matter of opportunity.

—from Precepts
attributed to
Hippocrates

Where the Doctors Are

The doctor shortage is shorter in some places than in others. If there are any hypochondriacs in Alaska they have a pretty poor chance of finding a nearby doctor to listen to their imaginary woes. According to the most recent census figures, there are 69 doctors to every 100,000 Alaskans.

Of course, this is still better than the doctor-patient ratio in Puerto Rico, where for every 100,000 people there are only 63 physicians.

The national average, by the way, is 149 doctors for every 100,000 Americans, based on an estimated 300,000 doctors currently at work in the U. S. Offhand, this sounds pretty comforting, nearly a third of a million doctors for 200 million people. But if you dig a little into the census figures, you see it isn't quite that way.

For example, about 5 percent of these doctors are retired. Another 5 to 7 percent are in federal service, usually in administrative or investigative work of far-reaching general importance. But few deal with individual patients. Another 10 to 12 percent are in various other governmental services at the state, county or municipal level, once again rarely dealing with individual sick people. Fifteen percent are interns or residents, still learning their trade but at least helping with some individual patients. Finally, about 65 percent are in private practice.

When we redo the arithmetic, what we actually have is less than 200,000 doctors in private practice for about 200 million people. This brings the private-care ratio down below an average of 100 doctors per 100,000 people, or less than one per thousand, if you wish.

The census, however, doesn't make the private-practice distinction when it ranks the states in order of their doctor-to-patient ratios. The absolute best place in the U. S. to fall ill, according to the census, is Washington, D. C., where there are 357 doctors per 100,000 people. On second glance, it turns out that most of these M.D.'s are not treating individual patients. Only 183 per 100,000 do private practice.

Well, then, what's really the best state? New York, not too surprisingly, turns out to head the list with 207 doctors per 100,000 people.

Massachusetts runs a close second with 196. Connecticut comes in third with 180 and in California, where old age and sunshine battle each other for the health of the citizenry, there are 178 doctors per 100,000 bronzed inhabitants.

Incidentally, it isn't necessarily the massing of a large number of people in a state that makes its doctor-patient ratio high, although it's one factor. While the two most populous states, New York and California, are near the top, so is Vermont, with 172, Colorado with 169, Maryland with 158, Oregon with 150, Pennsylvania with 153 and Rhode Island with 152.

Those states notably below the national average of 149 are nearly all underdeveloped areas or regions of extremely sparse or spread-out populations. I've already noted Puerto Rico and Alaska as having the poorest ratios. In ascending order we find the third lowest, South Dakota with 73, on up through Mississippi, Alabama, South Carolina, Arkansas, Idaho, Kentucky, New Mexico, North Dakota and Wyoming with 93.

I have tried to find some definite pattern in this. Per capita income provides rough correlations, but the presence of money doesn't automatically guarantee a high doctor-patient ratio, although it helps. What does seem to explain the way the states rank is a combination of population, money and one other factor: good medical schools.

In a very real sense, of course, it is manifestly unfair that the states with the best ratios should continue to attract the greatest number of medical students, holding them there with the promise of more people to serve and more money to make. But these are the facts. The way things are developing, Mach II jetliners will soon bring Los Angeles an hour from New York. We will then see the day when people who can afford it, whether they live in Saddle Sore, Montana, or Catfish, Mississippi, hop a plane and get topnotch medical treatment an hour later at one of the big centers in New York, Massachusetts or California.

What this does to the state of medicine back in Saddle Sore is not fit to think about. The town will consider itself lucky to have its own veterinarian.

George Won't Do It

I had occasion recently to spend some time with a maiden aunt of mine, a well-preserved party of more than seventy who may yet outlive me. She makes her home in a small efficiency apartment in Evanston where her medical needs are catered to by a general practitioner with whom I went to high school. Let's call him George.

He was an extremely bright young fellow when I first knew him and nothing he's done since has failed to shake that impression. I saw no reason not to recommend him to Aunt Millie and, for years, she saw no reason to complain of the recommendation.

"That friend of yours, George," she told me on my most recent visit. "Some doctor he's turned out to be."

"Going bad?" I asked with the vaguely deaf kind of sympathy you muster in such a situation.

"I used to call him for an appointment, get there on time and go right in to see him. Now I make an appointment and when I get there, half a dozen people are lined up ahead of me."

"Busy man."

"Busy not doing anything," she remarked cryptically.

"Aunt Millie, I always thought he was the original guy they meant when they said 'let George do it.' "

She shook her head. "George won't do it. Not anymore. Whatever I've got, he takes one look and for ten dollars tells me he has to send me to a specialist." She eyed me rather closely. "If you stop a policeman on the street and ask him where the railroad station is, should he charge you ten dollars to point the way?"

What I then told Aunt Millie probably went in one ear and out the other. I told her medical science had progressed so far that no one man could hope to know it all, that there were specialists in every field and even they had to hustle and sacrifice to keep up with their own fields. A doctor like George, a G.P., was more of a traffic cop than Millie realized. His job actually was to take a quick look at the problem and direct it to its proper destination, the specialist who had the knowledge and experience to handle the case.

"So why go to a G.P.?" Millie asked then.

She could, with as much validity, have asked why any medical student should any longer become a G.P. The statistics tell us the general man is dying out. Two decades ago, 80 percent of the medical population of the country was made up of general practitioners. Today only a third of the doctors in the U. S. are G.P.'s. To put it the other way, the percentage of specialists has risen from 20 to 66 in only about 20 years.

Why is there such an overwhelming preference among today's young doctors for a specialty practice, which requires much additional study, rather than a general one? Unlike some problems we face in medicine, there seems to be little economic reason underlying this one. A popular G.P. can make even more in fees and kickbacks than a specialist. Because he has direct contact with the patient and the family, he controls the entire case from diagnosis through operation to recovery. The confidence he inspires in his patients gives him complete control. Why should a young doctor pass up such an opportunity?

Chief among the valid reasons is the fact that with the tremendous knowledge explosion in medicine, few students feel they can in good conscience pretend to know what a G.P. seems to have to know and obviously doesn't.

Consider his daily routine. If it is extremely difficult for the specialist to keep abreast of his field, it is virtually impossible for a G.P. to know all fields. The typical general man, 20 to 25 years in practice, knows not a whit more than when he finished his internship. He's attended no lectures, taken no courses, participated in no conferences, made no hospital rounds, read no publications. What little he knows about current trends in general medicine is spoon-fed him by the so-called "detail men."

Detail men are field salesmen for drug houses. They spend time with individual doctors, put them on mailing lists for a variety of flashily produced literature and send them tons of samples. They give them free subscriptions to publications purporting to present medical news which, upon close examination, turn out to be prepared by a particular drug company or its public relations or advertising agency.

The detail men hope that by making the G.P. feel he is really being kept in the current swim, he will prescribe their drugs over those of their competitors. And, of course, he does.

He may have enough innate intelligence left to realize that

the gift horses being pressed on him must be looked in the mouth. He may still be bright enough to understand that a publication sponsored by a drug manufacturer cannot be anyone's idea of an impartial and ethical source of information. But most of the time he's overworked, undertaught and tired as hell. So he meets the detail man halfway and everybody's happy.

Rather than go that route, some medical students elect a specialty that keeps them at one remove from the public and holds the detail men at arm's length. This, as I have said, has its positive aspects. It has its negative ones, too.

We speak of the current generation of youngsters as alienated, aloof, uncommitted and, above all, "cool." I have no idea if they are all or any of that, any more than I know what goes through the minds of 38 people who watch a woman being murdered and who refuse to call the police.

There is no question but that the proliferation of information in the medical field has introduced a strongly impersonal note in the practice of medicine. It is more efficient, for example, to bring a patient to the hospital than to make house calls; many more patients can be served in the same time by one doctor if they are in a single, well-equipped place rather than their homes. But I am beginning to believe that it just doesn't have to be all that impersonal. I am slowly reaching the conclusion that a generation of doctors is coming to the fore which actually welcomes the impersonal and shies away from the direct contact the family doctor had with his patients.

The fact is, as we will see, that there is more to the healing art than the crisp, efficient treatment dealt out assembly-line style in most hospitals today by doctors who neither know their patients nor care to. Medically, what these organization-doctors prescribe is infinitely sounder than the by-guess-and-by-God treatment of yesterday's family doctor. But there is always a strong emotional element in these doctor-patient relationships that it is unwise to ignore and deadly to suppress.

The fact of the matter is—as many doctors have known for many centuries—that the "laying on" of hands cures ailments. If this sounds like witchcraft or lunacy, remember that three-quarters of the patients who visit a doctor are not really sick or would get well even if they hadn't seen him. Obviously, with such patients, laying on of hands or the right tone of voice or a friendly glance or a pat on the back or almost any kind of positive contact with the authority-image represented by the doctor will effect a cure.

This is one of the principles, incidentally, behind the rather well-known success of the placebo. A wide variety of tests have been conducted over the years with placebos, inert pills containing milk sugar or cornstarch. It has been proved again and again that almost as many people get well from this "nothing" treatment as from identical pills containing a specific remedy. Injections of pure distilled water can produce cures as effectively as injections loaded with beneficial drugs, serums or antibiotics.

Are we dealing with self-delusion on the part of the feeble-minded? Is there an element of magic in the doctor's art? What we actually have here are the very same kind of inter-personal reactions and side effects that we note in other person-to-person relationships but which, in the medical relationship, tend to produce dramatic results.

More and more of today's young doctors shy away from that close a relationship. I'm not prepared to analyze all their reasons. There are days when even the best of us gets fed up with the parade of humanity passing through our offices.

To think of a whole new era of depersonalized medicine, assembly line in nature, is somewhat depressing. Considering the population explosion and the doctor shortage, it may be the only sensible way of providing adequate medical care for the world's billions. It may be the only workable way of putting into practice the great discoveries taking place every day in modern medical research. It may be the only way to guarantee decent care for the impoverished and the lower middle class. It may well be all of these good things.

But my Aunt Millie won't like it.

A Fee Grows in Brooklyn

Dr. Sam Sloan had a heart of mush. He loved the people of Brooklyn and worked long hours healing them. In the process he became a millionaire several times over and narrowly escaped jail. That I should have been even remotely instrumental in keeping him out of prison is a source of wonder to me, even now, decades after the event.

I was in that no-man's-land between residency and building up a private practice that would sustain life—my own. Suddenly, almost out of the blue, came the most amazing opportunity. Still under thirty-five years of age, I was being offered the post of chief of obstetrics and gynecology at the extremely prestigious-sounding Brooklyn International Hospital . . . all this to a country boy from Chicago not too long out of his residency in New York who still hardly knew one end of the island from the other.

Brooklyn International! This glorious name, redolent of status, was a private hospital of advanced years, situated in a lower-income area of Brooklyn among families with a strong tradition of grown sons and daughters living in or near the house of their parents.

Only a block away from Brooklyn International were the offices of Sam Sloan, M.D. I say offices, since he occupied three entire floors of a six-story double-front apartment building. The lower floors were clogged with every conceivable kind of physiotherapy apparatus. Row upon row of back-stretchers, buttocks-pounders and arm-exercisers faded off into the distance as one viewed the lower floors. And, seated or standing in the grip of each machine, there was a beady-browed patient doing what Sloan had told him he must do.

On the top floor, Sam Sloan and two assistants saw not 10, not 50, but between 100 and 200 patients a day. Consider the arithmetic for a moment. Since many of his patients worked all day, Sloan opened his offices at 7 A.M. and closed them after 8 P.M., a 13-hour day with an hour off for lunch. On a busy day, in 720 minutes, Sloan and his men gave each of his 200 patients an average of 3 minutes and 36 seconds. Deduct from this the time it takes to exchange both greetings and good-byes—Sam Sloan had a big heart and put great stock in such amenities—and you come up with a good, solid 120 seconds in which to examine each lucky patient. On a slow day they got an extra minute.

It is axiomatic in the medical business that when you invest as much money as Sloan did in physiotherapy apparatus, naturally a great many of your patients turn out to need physiotherapy. More important: except in extreme cases, physiotherapy can be counted on not to injure the patients unduly, especially since most of them are entirely well to begin with.

But Sam Sloan's goodheartedness extended even further than that. Although a great many of his patients required physiotherapy, an even greater number needed drugs and medicines of one kind or another. Sloan's prescriptions were always handed over with the following admonition: "Get this filled right now. Take it down the block to Brooklyn International Hospital. Their pharmacy knows exactly what to do."

Result: the waiting lines at Sloan's office were not much longer than the waiting lines at the Brooklyn International Hospital's pharmacy.

The astute reader has already seen the light. Sam Sloan's effulgence shone over the entire neighborhood. He owned Brooklyn International Hospital—and its pharmacy.

Fortunately for the general health of the neighborhood, Brooklyn International was a rather small hospital with some 50 beds. Sloan and others kept them permanently filled with a steady parade of patients whose condition was too serious for physiotherapy, too advanced for medication from the pharmacy. Indicated treatment: surgery. He used two outside surgeons for his "nothing work," and skimmed off a third of their fees.

Sloan was averaging 60,000 office calls a year. At $5 a call, this part of the operation alone was grossing a quarter of a million dollars. To this add physiotherapy fees, pharmacy revenue, hospital charges, surgery fees, the cost of anesthetics, medication, tests, etc., and you were well over a million-dollar-volume figure.

But Sam Sloan's beneficence was trammeled and he felt the restriction keenly. Motherhood was a major industry in this section of Brooklyn and Sloan wasn't able to cut into the maternity melon unless he could replace his physiotherapy-pill-surgery image with a shiny new general-hospital-type façade.

Over a period of years, Sloan acquired suitable nearby land and eventually constructed a fairly modest one-story building of whitewashed cinder block which bore the resounding name of the Bertha E. Sloan Memorial Women's Pavilion. All heart, Sloan had named the storefront structure after the woman most responsible for bringing him to his patients, his mother.

There remained now only a few small details such as getting approval from the Board of Health and the Department of Hospitals. To do this, Sloan had to satisfy certain minimum requirements as to physical plant and professional staff. Knowing nothing of obstetrics or gynecology, but well aware of what the medical powers-that-be knew of his background, Sloan decided to buy respectability in the form of a well-trained, well-recommended young doctor, a stranger to New York, who wasn't too bright. Me.

I set to work laying out floor plans, making lists of equipment, hiring help. Although I should have known better, I hadn't a moment's worry about where patients would come from, how much they should pay, or for what complaints they would be treated. Instead, I concentrated on the technical routine of setting up a hospital that would win official approval. And, of course, it did.

With that hurdle passed, Sloan moved into high gear. Too often in the past he had to content himself with giving female patients a course in physiotherapy or a regimen of pink pills. Now he was ready for the big leagues.

But a strange thing happened. Although trained as a surgeon and—in the pardonable stupidity of youth—accounting myself a rather deft one, I was rarely asked to handle the flow of gynecological surgery cases that now began to flow through the Bertha E. Sloan Memorial Women's Pavilion.

The few cases I was called on to attend fell into a regular pattern which I only dimly perceived at first. In most instances, these were patients in bad trouble who had gotten that way after a previous bout of medical attention. The case of Mona R. contains enough of the elements to serve as a typical example.

Mona's trouble began during my first month as chief of obstetrics. I heard my name being paged over the public address system and I lifted my nose out of the floor plans and equipment lists to rush to the emergency room.

An examination was hardly necessary. One could almost smell what the trouble was and a quick glance confirmed the situation. Mona R. had been discharged a week before after having delivered a perfectly normal baby boy in a perfectly normal way under the minimal ministrations of Sam Sloan, M.D., himself.

The fact that Sloan was, at best, a general practitioner many decades out of school who had never done a residency in obstetrics did not mean, under New York State law, that he could not deliver a baby. If midwives could, so could Sloan. More to the point, in the vast majority of births almost any intelligent person with well-scrubbed hands can bring forth a perfectly stunning specimen of babyhood at no risk to the mother. Nature is like that.

So Mona's birth had been a normal one, with perhaps a bit of manipulation necessary at the very beginning when the actual birth started. Sloan had, perhaps, spread a little here and delved a little there. All perfectly normal.

In the process, Sam Sloan, M.D., had created a fistula between the rectum and the vagina, a leak through which feces had entered the vagina. This had set up an extremely messy situation.

My job: repair the fistula. I suggested that we wait, that, in fact, we had no choice but to wait. Sloan ruled otherwise. He wanted Mona over and done with and forgotten. So, against my better judgment, I did it Sloan's way . . . fast. It took two tries over a period of several weeks during which time we also treated the infection. Finally, after a few more weeks in the Bertha E. Sloan Memorial Women's Pavilion, Mona R. was discharged on the road to full recovery.

That afternoon, Sloan came around to see me with an envelope which he handed across my desk. "Your fee as surgeon, Doctor." I counted $200 in tens and twenties.

I have reason to know more about Mona R. than I learned from this initial encounter. Years later she came to me as a private patient. I saw her through two additional births, both of which had to be done by Caesarean section because of the unreliable wall between vagina and rectum. Finally, Mona required a hysterectomy. It is my opinion that the two Caesarean sections and the hysterectomy could have been avoided if the wall could have been relied on. The fact that I was unwilling to take that chance, even though I had done the original repair, made the rest of the surgery necessary. Sloan's original carelessness cost Mona R. more than a decade of gynecological trouble and expense.

But it cost her more than that, as I eventually learned. At the time of her successful discharge from the hospital, and for a few months afterwards, I continued to live in a world of ignorant bliss. But events can finally penetrate even the fattest head. A glimmering of what I was doing at the Bertha E. Sloan Memorial Women's Pavilion began to take shape. I began to see myself as a figurehead, a front man and, when it came right down to it, a patsy who was no better, for being ignorant, than the corrupt man who paid me.

It was at this point that I fired off a very well-written letter of resignation, complete with suggestions for bettering the pavilion: "Tear it down and put in a supermarket," was one of them.

Seven years later, the Department of Hospitals finally caught up with Sloan, who had let conditions in the pavilion and the hospital grow so flagrant that even a bribable inspector could no longer wink at them. Both Brooklyn International Hospital and the Bertha E. Sloan Memorial Women's Pavilion were padlocked by the city. Sloan escaped jail on several technicalities, one of the least important being that the pavilion itself had seemed to be in better shape than the hospital because it had apparently been organized and set up on a sounder basis. Somewhere in Florida, or it may be the Bahamas, Sam Sloan, M.D., has retired to enjoy the lush fruits of a life devoted to healing.

The story has a postscript. Shortly after Sloan's brush with the law, many years after I'd left him, Mona R. sought me out as her obstetrician. During our first interview we discussed many things, including my fees.

"I'm better off financially than I was that first time," she assured me.

"That's all right. My fees are reasonable."

She eyed me for a moment. "It depends what you mean by

reasonable," she said then. "It took me two years to pay off your surgery bill last time."

"My bill"—I bristled—"or the hospital's?"

She nodded very definitely. "There were two bills. The hospital charges were fifteen hundred dollars."

"That's high," I said, "but you needed a lot of care."

"And the surgery fee was fifteen hundred dollars."

For a long moment I didn't trust myself to speak. When I'd calmed down enough, I contented myself with a cryptic reply.

"I think," I said, "you'll find my fee much lower now. The medical profession owes you something."

Dr. Sincere

In advertising, being sincere is supposed to go a long way. In medicine the best way to apply sincerity is with a trowel. I give you Jacques St. Cyr, M.D.

None of us ever found out if the name was real. He had no French accent. If anything, one could hear in his voice the faint notes of a Bronx childhood. But the name on his diplomas and certificates was Jacques St. Cyr and, for all I know, his pedigree could have reached back into the mists of time to some lost dauphin in the bayous of Louisiana.

The Dr. St. Cyr we knew was a tall, well-built man with coal-black hair that had glints of blue in it, a square, good-looking face and lots of awfully white teeth. He resembled a much more handsome Cary Grant. When you met him in the doctors' lounge or along a corridor or at a seminar, his dark eyes would fix yours, he would stare deeply into your very soul and smile, unleashing teeth that rapidly blinded you.

"Hi, there, fella," he'd say and you would respond with a weak, "Hi ya, Jake," having just received some eternal truth from on high.

St. Cyr was well connected, As a general surgeon he operated only on prominent and well-to-do people. He also served as staff physician for an extremely posh Chicago hotel and a major league ball club. Although other doctors worked under him on such jobs, during the baseball season St. Cyr himself would cancel all operations but those commanding the highest fees while he ministered to gravely wounded outfielders in whatever city they had fallen.

He had two endearing characteristics which put him high on the list of every doctor who knew him and every patient he served—although the titles of the lists would differ somewhat. Before describing his behavior, however, let me point out almost parenthetically that the resident surgeons on whom he would call to assist him in his operations usually tossed a coin beforehand. Loser scrubbed with St. Cyr.

As a surgeon, Jake St. Cyr was not to be believed. He could do a mediocre appendectomy, but about anything more complex he was totally ignorant. Of specialties like thoracic surgery or orthopedic surgery he knew nothing, had no background, no training and no ability. Yet, of course, he took on exactly these kinds of operations. Invariably the resident would have to keep St. Cyr out of trouble, if he could.

In addition to saving the patient's life and making St. Cyr look good, the resident had another role which many outright refused to play. In that case an intern or a nurse took over as understudy. It was a dramatic role indeed. As soon as the operation was over and the patient wheeled away, someone had the job of draping a blanket over St. Cyr's broad shoulders and handing him a tall glass of orange juice, freshly squeezed. The script, apparently, called for the audience to realize that surgery was a taxing job which utterly drained one of strength. The blanket was to fend off shock, I suppose, and the orange juice was to replenish St. Cyr's body glucose. Or something.

In any event, St. Cyr would march around the corridors, an imposing sight, having done nothing much more than watch a resident do his operation for him, while orderlies and nurses, visitors and patients, marveled at the inner strength of the man, the intense dedication, the terrible chances he took with his own resources, etc., *ad. naus.*

But St. Cyr didn't rely solely on this general type of self-advertisement. In the parlance of Madison Avenue, moping around in a blanket and slugging orange juice was only good enough for the general run of rubes, a "buckshot" approach designed to hit a lot of people with light impact. But for the sharpshooting approach that sent a slug right into the heart of the bull's-eye, St. Cyr had developed another technique.

As soon after surgery as his patient was able to hear words and understand them, St. Cyr would show up in the sickroom, blanket on or blanket off. He would then sit down *on the edge of the bed.* His glance would transfix the patient's woozy orbs. If the patient were a woman, St. Cyr would hold her hand. Men he patted on the arm or shoulder. (I once saw him with a patient who was wearing several casts; St. Cyr had nowhere to pat him but his belly, which he did.) Having established ocular and physical contact, St. Cyr would unhinge that dazzling smile of his and proceed to give his patient the straight-from-the-heart talk.

"I just wanted you to know what a lucky person you are. You may be the luckiest human being in the whole world. Why, when we went in there, I can't begin to describe what we found."

But he could. And did. He would take the patient over the hurdles and through the thickets and across the water jumps of some of the fanciest surgery never performed. The operation he described was one St. Cyr couldn't have done. Neither could a team of top surgeons. It combined adventure with suspense, ghoulishness with sex, blood with guts, in short, all the elements of a best-seller.

For that was what St. Cyr really was, after all, a best-selling doctor. Once he finished conning his patient she was convinced that she owed her very life to this tall, handsome, tired man, that no one else in the Free World could have done what he did and that God Almighty would have paid money to scrub with him.

Among a certain class of patient, therefore, the class that begins around the $50,000-a-year income level, there was only one surgeon to have and having him was as much a mark of status as where you had your summer place and where you wintered. The fact that his surgical adventures were entirely spurious and that most of his operations were performed by whatever resident was handy made not the slightest difference. It was St. Cyr who wore the blanket, drank the orange juice (freshly squeezed), sat down *on the bed* and told the long, thrilling tale.

Still a commanding and impressive figure today, in his late fifties, St. Cyr no longer serves as surgeon for the local ball club. He will tell you his schedule became too heavy for this kind of work.

"After all," he says, "I have really sick patients, people to whom my skill can make the difference between life and death, not a few prima donna outfielders with imaginary nervous complaints." He says this kind of thing with a self-depreciating smile of striking sincerity. Well, let's see.

There was a time about ten years ago when the major league in which this Chicago club played was dominated by the name and game of one man, Clay Blount. Today's twelve-year-olds still remember Clay Blount, even though he hasn't played in a decade. But the mark he placed on the game, his style of playing, the way he handled himself and the immense talent he had on the diamond would have put him in the

Hall of Fame even if he hadn't led his league in batting, RBIs, bases stolen, put-outs and home runs. You can still buy Clay Blount bats, balls, mitts, caps and sunglasses even though the man whose signature they bear hasn't put on a baseball suit in ten years and won't either.

Early one season, Blount's knee went bad. It had been bothering him all the previous year, slowing up his work in the World Series and giving him quite a lot of pain over the winter. The usual treatment that coaches and trainers could give him would only limber up the joint for a while before it would knot with pain again.

We know that legitimate differences of opinion can exist among honest men in every walk of life. They exist among doctors, too. It is possible, in Clay Blount's case, to say that there might have been several other approaches which should first have been tried before resorting to surgery. That is a matter of opinion. But having once decided that surgery was necessary, there is no question at all, no room for any difference of opinion, about the fact that the best possible orthopedic surgeon was to be used.

Clay Blount was a nationwide figure, the idol of youngsters everywhere, the mainstay of his club and his league. He was the epitome of the good sportsman. His name will continue to come up whenever baseball is written about or discussed for many, many years to come. For economic reasons, for cultural reasons—even for political reasons when you remember Blount's popularity abroad—and for every humane reason as well, the best orthopedic surgeon was obviously the only man to work on Blount's knee.

The decision made by the team surgeon, Jacques St. Cyr, M.D., was that he himself could and would perform the operation. Whereupon he did. And what the seven other clubs in the league had been trying to do for 15 years, St. Cyr did in half an hour: he put Clay Blount out of baseball forever. Blount was unable ever again to run or hit.

The operation was performed out of town, so I have been unable to determine whether, afterwards, St. Cyr donned his blanket and quaffed his orange juice, freshly squeezed.

But of one thing I am certain: after the operation he sat down *on Blount's bed,* patted his shoulder and made him feel like the luckiest ballplayer in the world.

That's what I call sincere.

...that into whatsoever house I shall enter, it shall be for the good of the sick to the utmost of my power, holding myself aloof from wrong, from corruption, from the tempting of others to vice....

—from the Oath of
Hippocrates

Diagnosis: Blue Cross

Medical mythology, in addition to its stock tales of make-shift operations in the wilderness and other dramatic rescues from death's door, has one standard character that warms everyone's heart. He's the kindly old physician—I picture him with a tobacco-stained moustache and somewhat loose suspenders instead of a belt—who never was much at book-larnin' and fancy modern ideas. He relied on a mystic sixth sense. He could look at a patient, shuffle from side to side and then diagnose some totally unexpected ailment which, of course, always turned out to be so.

If he ever existed, this particular character is now extremely dead. In his place is a highly trained specialist, the modern diagnostician. I had a call from one example of this breed the other day.

"This is Artie French," he said. "A lady was in here to see me with a sort of a pain." Silence.

"A sort of a pain," I prompted.

"She's got two health insurance policies," Artie said then.

"You mentioned a pain?"

"I mean it, two kinds. She's got Blue Cross and Blue Shield at her office and her husband's got John Hancock Major Medical at his office."

Dr. Arthur French is an extremely respected diagnostician in his circle, beloved by a bevy of general practitioners who find it easier to send a patient to Artie to hear bad, expensive news.

"What kind of pain?" I persisted.

"So I'm sending her around. She'll be calling you this afternoon."

The G.P.-to-specialist play, designed to escalate medical charges, is a good, if crude, method of sharing the patient's wealth. The addition of a diagnostician to make a G.P.-to-diagnostician-to-specialist sequence constitutes a rather sophisticated double play. The essentially healthy patient enriches three doctors instead of two, keeping all three under a gentleman's obligation to refer business back as early and as often as possible. Health insurance pays for most of this.

With Artie, his associates and thousands of others who think as they do, the situation is always the same—Diagnosis: Blue Cross.

A lot has been written and said about health insurance, its constantly rising costs, its inability to meet the needs of reality. Prior to the war, only about 12 million Americans had health insurance of any kind. Even this was rudimentary, usually a way of prepaying some small part of hospitalization charges.

Today, only a quarter of a century later, about 150 million Americans have some form of health insurance coverage. And while this growth is amazing—because most of it has been achieved voluntarily—we should not pause too long for back-patting. Most of these 150 million Americans don't have full protection. It's partial, often spotty. Those who enjoy rather broad coverage against most medical, hospital and surgical bills number a more modest 35 million. Even so, this is quite an accomplishment. Or is it?

Who is still excluded from full protection? Those who can't afford to buy health insurance. Are they many of the same people who can't afford medical care on any basis? Yes. For the sad fact is that insurance is not a new way of medical treatment, but simply a new way of paying for it. It is only

slightly different than putting aside money in a savings ac-
count to pay for future medical expenses. It is simply a form
of prepayment with certain added features. Those who can't
afford payment certainly can't afford prepayment.

What's more, like other forms of insurance, health insurance is being very badly abused by our fellow Americans
who have no one but themselves to blame for the generally
rising costs of all kinds of coverage.

The jury that awards a fantastic sum of damages to the
crippled plaintiff or the family of the deceased goes home that
night and sleeps in peace. It has done an unusually good deed.
It has rewarded a victim without punishing anybody. The
defendant was insured, wasn't he? It isn't his money. It's just
insurance money.

If I explain to you that this is one reason why insurance
costs go up, you see the logic of it. Big claims payments equal
big premiums.

But suppose you go to your doctor with a nagging pain
in the lower back. He asks if you're covered by hospitalization insurance and you say yes. He thereupon puts you in
the hospital for a week instead of sending you home to rest
for a week. Questionable treatment like that raises the cost
of your health insurance and everyone else's.

Your first reaction might be: "If that's the case, isn't the
doctor cutting off his nose to spite his face? By forcing up
insurance costs, isn't he making it harder for more people to
have more health insurance so he can have more patients?"

The answer is no, for several reasons. Health insurance
costs are split more or less equally between an employer and
an employee. You feel a rate rise only half as sharply that
way. What's more, the idea of health insurance is ingrained
in our society. No self-respecting American with middle-class
pretensions would possibly be without it.

There's more to the answer. The doctor who needlessly
refers a patient to a hospital is creating business for the hos-

pital. In this respect the economics of running a profit-making hospital resembles that of running a hotel: keep those beds filled. The doctor who fills beds is a favored doctor. His hospital loves him and will go to almost any lengths to keep him happy.

For instance, it will let him do almost any kind of operation, providing he keeps the hospital records clean and his patients can pay. Which brings us to one of the prime reasons hospitalization and health insurance rates keep soaring.

Let's contrast two institutions, Hospital A, a fairly reputable place connected with a medical school, and Hospital B, a private hospital owned by a doctor or group of doctors. Both are acceptable to all the various hospitalization plans but for the sake of this exercise in basic arithmetic, we will call the insurance plan Red Badge. Catchy.

Hospital A is a big voluntary hospital with more than 1,500 beds. In it a variety of well-known doctors operate, teach, see patients, handle ward duties. Its equipment and laboratories are extensive. It is the place where a number of techniques have been developed and have spread throughout the medical profession. It serves patients of all ages, all problems and both sexes.

Hospital B is a private institution with 50 beds, no labs worthy of the name and very little equipment. If you examine its records for the past five years you find a very strange thing: the overwhelming proportion of its patients—at least 80 percent—are women between the ages of twenty-five and thirty-five.

One of the techniques perfected at Hospital A is a rather widely known operation developed by a Dr. Smith and called a Smith Suspension. In the past five years the big voluntary hospital where it was perfected has done perhaps 50 Smith Suspensions.

The Smith Suspension, for you lay people, requires that

the abdominal wall be opened and a certain kind of stitch be put in to link a certain organ to a certain spot.

The virtues of the Smith Suspension are many. It is simple, almost minor surgery, rapid, easy to perform, easy to recover from. What's even better, a gynecologist can decide on a Smith Suspension at his own discretion, without anyone raising an eyebrow. Best of all, there is no tissue removed, nothing for the pathologist to examine.

In the past five years, as I have said, 50 Smith Suspensions have been done at Hospital A, the place it was developed, where 1,500 beds await the ill of Chicago. In the same five years, at Hospital B with its 50 beds and peculiarly specialized clientele, 400 Smith Suspensions have been done, 394 of them paid by Red Badge, because the insurance plan recognizes the Smith Suspension as an operation for which it will pay.

Let's assume that care provided by Hospital B has been rated by Red Badge at $35 a day. Let's also assume that the young ladies who desperately need Smith Suspensions are required to stay in Hospital B for an average of a week. Red Badge thus pays about $245 for the average Smith Suspension. In the past five years Red Badge has paid out nearly $100,000 for Smith Suspensions at Hospital B.

Multiply Hospital B by perhaps 50, the number of other, similar private hospitals in Red Badge's business area, some larger or smaller than Hospital B, but all equally devoted to operations of the suspension type done on young women. That's $5 million in five years, or a million a year that Red Badge has paid out for . . . what?

Surgeons have a name for this type of work. They call it a "nothing operation." It may be written up in the hospital's records as a suspension, or it may be given the legitimate, Red Badge-approved name of half a dozen other harmless operations. The point is that this surgery is never written down on the records under its right name: sterilization. It is never recorded as a ligation, or tube-tying. Because Red Badge won't pay for a ligation. No insurance plan will.

Question One: why so many of these operations? Don't these young women know about the Pill or the Coil? The answers to this question are many. They lie partly in certain cultural or religious diffidences. They can also be found in the fact that ligation is thought to be absolutely sure, while the other methods may not be. But probably the single most important reason is that Red Badge will not pay for the Pill or the Coil. But it will pay for a "nothing operation," to the tune of $1 million a year.

Question Two: why, in all these years, haven't Red Badge inspectors and medical supervisors spotted this kind of fraud and stopped it? Why do they continue approving huge payouts that force rates higher?

Answer: one need not be a medical person to detect this fraud. One need only be a statistician, comparing patient and surgery records of two institutions such as Hospital A and Hospital B. The obvious facts leap out of the ledger pages at even the least sophisticated observer. The fact that they have yet to leap out at a Red Badge investigator tends to suggest that Red Badge's people are either terribly stupid or terribly corrupt.

It is easy, of course, to scorn the Red Badge people for winking at this wholesale fraud. But it is that nice lady next door to you who does the actual asking for a ligation. And it's her friendly family G.P. who recommends a specialist. It's the specialist who brings her to Hospital B where it's the nurses, the orderlies, the pathologist, the anesthetist and the owners who conspire to keep the records innocuously clean. The Red Badge investigator is pretty much low man on the Corruption Totem Pole. But his connivance makes everything "free" by shifting the burden of payment to Red Badge, from whom all blessings flow.

We have come a long way since that day when only one

out of every dozen Americans had any form of health insurance protection. Today, three in every four enjoy this coverage, to a greater or lesser extent, and one assumes our health as a nation must surely be the better for it.

Like so many good things, however, health insurance has proved much too tempting. Whatever its inherent potential good, it is today one of the prime reasons corrupt medicine flourishes. It bankrolls a majority of the frauds by which doctors mulct patients. It is a horn of plenty from which blessings flow, along with many, many abuses.

Doctor Without Patients

It was that dapper old fraud, Hagen, who first alerted me to the importance of the hospital pathologist.

It was Hagen's standard procedure, when operating on a patient, to perform a small skit to which we residents had given the title "Showing the Tumor, a Comedy in One Act," performed for his patients, most of whom were under spinal anesthesia and, though groggy, remained conscious.

Regardless of what the particular operation was all about —and with Hagen it could range from a total and complete "nothing" operation all the way to a total hysterectomy actually performed by his assistant—Hagen eventually concluded with the following:

HAGEN: (*grabbing up a normal uterus, the bloodier the better, and dropping it onto a towel*) Here. Show the patient the tumor!

Which was done, of course. Hagen was a full attending physician and no one crossed him. Besides, he really wasn't a vicious person, merely completely venal and utterly corrupt. But, as I have said of him in an earlier place, he at least had the sense to let competent doctors handle his cases for him.

You must understand that Hagen had no idea, at the time of the operation, whether or not he would claim it as a removal of a tumor or what-have-you. But he never neglected setting up a tumor-type situation in case he needed it. Each and every one of his patients was confronted with some gory stump of horror and forced to recoil weakly. Later they would swear to the size and shape of the "tumor." Hagen took no chances. Since he just might have to claim a tumor after all, there was no sense in being unprepared.

This is by way of introducing the one doctor in the hospital who has no patients, the pathologist. He works tucked away in a lab where he studies tissue sent him from every operation, determines its condition, the state of its cells, the presence of infection, etc. It is the pathologist who tells your surgeon whether the tumor he has removed was malignant or benign.

His job is, thus, an extremely responsible one. In most reputable hospitals he makes about a third of what he could make in private practice. Because pathologists come fully equipped, like all good Americans, with a wife and kids who have been taught that doctors make three times as much a year without half trying, many pathologists find other work to do. They moonlight by taking night calls for other doctors who have given up healing during prime TV time. They also moonlight by doing pathology for small private hospitals who can't afford their own pathologist and, in any event, want the protection of a reputable man's name signed to their reports. In these and other ways, if the pathologist's constitution can take an 18-hour working day, he can afford to work as a pathologist.

I should explain at this point that, no matter what one of Hagen's patients might believe, there are only a limited number of organs in the abdominal cavity and thus only a limited number of places for pathology or disease to develop.

In both men and women, for example, we find the liver, spleen, gall bladder, stomach, intestine and the like, while, in a separate area lie the kidneys, ureter and bladder. Women have a few more expendable ingredients, but this is just about the sum and substance of what can be looked at, toyed with, tickled, cut, shortened, spliced, carved, whittled or removed.

The moment any tissue, no matter how small, is taken out of the patient, the scrub nurse passes it carefully to the circulating nurse who bottles it in a formalin fixative, tags it properly and sends it on its way to the pathology department. In a reputable hospital there are no exceptions to this routine. All tissue is saved. It cannot be discarded at the discretion of the surgeon. Only after a report is rendered by the pathologist can the tissue be thrown away. In a reputable hospital.

Thus the only way the omniscient pathologist can be outwitted or bypassed or left out of the picture at all is by not removing any tissue.

Now, according to what every doctor learns, there are very few operations in which tissue is not removed and, therefore, no specimen produced for pathological study. Among these rare operations is the surgery necessary to break up adhesions from previous operations or obstructions in ducts and intestines or to repair some hernias. Another reason for a no-tissue-removed operation—equally unusual—is a diagnostic mistake. What the doctor expected to find he does not find. There being nothing for him to remove, he sews up the patient with a mumbled "um, sorry about that." A third rare reason for this kind of surgery is where something is tied off or suspended with a stitch or two. The fallopian tubes can be tied off in this way, preventing ova from being fertilized. A tuck or two can be taken to link up the uterus to a nearby support, thus correcting a possibly abnormal position or posture which probably needed no correction.

These suspensions used to be very popular because it was the fad to believe that certain wombs were "tipped" or "prolapsed" or pointed in some wrong direction or other. We now believe that where this actually occurs there is some reason for it which neatly propping up the uterus will not cure. Suspensions of the womb are outmoded and distrusted. They are, nevertheless, one of the most frequent operations done in private hospitals, mainly because no tissue is removed and there is none to examine.

I recall one fairly competent and fairly honest general surgeon who was often called in by a G.P. and given what later turned out to be a highly imaginative history to substantiate some false problem. On delving into the innards and finding nothing wrong, the surgeon would invariably, and without a moment's hesitation, remove the patient's appendix.

"As long as I have to cut in," he would say, "it shouldn't be a total loss."

To give you an idea of how thoroughly a good, honest pathologist examines tissue sent him, let me quote, with some revisions, from a pathology report I received on a hysterectomy. It begins with the patient's name and hospital room number, my name, various pertinent dates and the number assigned to the specimen tissue. There follows a gross description:

> The specimen consists of a uterus and detached cervix and bilateral tubes and ovaries. Uterus weighs 820 gm and measures 21 x 14 x 10 cm. Shape is distorted by fibroids; myometrium contains multiple large fibroids, largest measuring 10 cm in diameter. Endometrial cavity is distorted by fibroids, whose cut surface is white, firm and whorled. Os is regular. Endocervical canal measures 3 cm in length and presents retention cysts. Representative sections taken for study.

The pathologist's report concludes with the results of his microscopic examination of thin sections of tissue:

Uterus: chronic cystic cervicitis, leiomyomas, secretory endometrium.
Fallopian tubes: chronic salpingitis.
Ovaries: Hemorrhagic corpus luteum, follicular cysts.

It isn't necessary that you know what all of that means. Suffice it to say that it justifies having removed the uterus and its paraphernalia. I should say, it justifies the removal as far as I am concerned. But the surgeon is not the only one, in a reputable hospital, who must be satisfied.

Every time tissue is removed, the pathologist makes a report on it. Every report is read by the chief or director on whose service the particular operation was performed. My pathology reports, for example, are reviewed by the chief of obstetrics and gynecology. But this checking process, in a reputable hospital, does not end there. A copy of every report also goes to the Tissue Committee, which reviews the findings and tries to determine whether or not the surgery was justified.

Let us assume that a particular surgeon has been performing "nothing" operations and passing them off in a variety of ways. The no-tissue-removed surgery, of course, may be awfully suspect, but neither his chief of service nor the Tissue Committee can prove anything, except that he does too many of them. Like the connection between lung cancer and cigarette smoking, it can only be proved statistically. In the absence of other proof, however, this will do. The "nothing" surgeon begins to vary his operations and remove some tissue. In effect, he tries to adjust his track record to remain free of suspicion. He's gambling that perhaps the pathology report will slip through unnoticed by the busy chief or committee. If it doesn't slip through, he gambles that he can talk his way out of it. Let's see how he fares.

It doesn't matter whether it's the chief or the committee that first becomes suspicious, because they tend to act in somewhat the same way. In a reputable hospital, if the committee tumbles to him first, they ask for additional information beyond the pathology report alone. They want to see the patient's chart and review the entire case as worked up by the resident.

If the surgeon in question has innocently performed an operation that excites this kind of attention, he doesn't really need any further warning. If this is one of his early excursions into corruption, his newfound career is considerably slowed up by even this mild interest in his doings. But if he's a dedicated "nothing" surgeon, he needs a stronger deterrent.

The next time one of his pathology reports excites the Tissue Committee's interest, they may not only ask for more information on the case, they may actually call him in. In a reputable hospital he must appear before the committee and things can get a bit sticky as he tries to worm his way out of a tight corner. Usually, on a second offense, if all else fails he can get away with calling it an honest mistake.

Because the villain of our piece is determined to get rich quick, a third occasion eventually arises. Once again the pathology report excites suspicion. Now the fat's in the fire. Not only will he be called in for interrogation by the committee, but he can no longer rely on the "mistake" alibi. He is "spoken to" rather bluntly. His only remedy now is never to be caught again.

What happens if he is? I have no idea. None of the surgeons I know have ever been stupid enough to endanger their affiliation that way. They take their "nothing" work elsewhere and do only legitimate operations in the reputable hospital.

What is elsewhere like? Don't the private hospitals where most "nothing" surgery is practiced have pathologists and Tissue Committees, too?

Why, of course. It's true, however, that the private hospital will tolerate hundreds of no-tissue-removed operations without a murmur of disbelief, thus making less work for the pathologist. It's also true that few, if any, have a resident pathologist. They usually farm out their work to an underpaid man at a nearby voluntary or public hospital. This man is a real study in conflicts. He needs the money the private hospital pays him. He hasn't the time to examine the tissue they send him as carefully as the tissue from his own hospital. And he suspects, or knows, that a lot of the tissue won't show any pathology. He also knows he won't be paid much longer once he starts rendering careful, honest pathology reports to the private hospital. The work will go to another pathologist. What to do?

Like any other human situation, a few go to extremes and the majority hug the center. A few refuse the work and keep their honor clean. A few revel in corruption, take on the work of two or three other private institutions and die rich. The majority cheats only a little, lies only a little, is only a little careless.

Even so, on occasion a no-pathology report comes through on surgery done in a private hospital. It makes its way to the Tissue Committee. The farce that ensues is richly comic.

These are offenders judging the offenses of other offenders. The air grows thick with fakery. High-minded arguments spring up. Judicious verdicts are painfully arrived at. Second chances are given. Extenuating circumstances are found. I would venture to guess that although the Tissue Committees of private hospitals meet once a week to fill the official records with the sound and fury of their staged deliberations, there is not one example extant of a surgeon being asked to take his business elsewhere as a result of these august deliberations.

At its very best, in a reputable voluntary or public hospital, the checks-and-balances system of the pathologist's report, scrutinized by the chief of service and the Tissue Committee, will result in warning away the most corrupt surgeons or of forcing them to do only necessary surgery within the hospital's walls.

At its very worst, usually in a private hospital, the combination of corrupt pathologist and corrupt Tissue Committee will result in the most terrible of surgical abuses. Because he has access to virtually any type of tissue in the hospital where he holds his regular job, the moonlighting pathologist can even supply tissue to match any request. He can become a sort of Central Casting Bureau, providing a fibroid where one is called for, a tumor here, a cyst there. When this happens, obviously the patient has only one precept to guide him as he enters the operating room:

"Abandon hope, all ye who enter here."

When bad physicians, who comprise the vast majority, treat men suffering from no serious disease—far more common than serious diseases—the greatest blunders do not affect patients seriously and physicians are not shown up in their true colors to laymen. Only when they meet with severe, violent and dangerous illness do their errors and lack of skill become manifest to all.

—from Precepts
attributed to
Hippocrates

Anatomy of a Private Hospital

Of the three types of hospitals, the private institution probably breeds the greatest corruption.

Public hospitals are set up specifically to treat poor patients
on a clinic basis. They charge no fees. Voluntary hospitals
charge fees to private patients but also provide free-clinic
treatment. They frequently have extensive teaching and research facilities as well.

But it is the private hospital or the private outpatient
clinic, owned by a single person or group and operated solely
for the enrichment of its owners, where needless surgery is
most frequently practiced, where health insurance fraud is
at its peak, where a tighter conspiracy of silence reigns, where
more patients are impoverished without medical cause but
for profit alone, where more illegal, quasi-legal and semilegal
operations are performed, where more useless but expensive
medication is prescribed and sold, where actual medical facilities are poorest, laboratory work most suspect, greater
numbers of the healthy kept in bed and where, finally, a
higher per-bed dollar volume and profit are generated than
in any other medical institution in the land.

Before examining the anatomy of a typical private hospital,
it might be a good idea to find out who patronizes such
establishments. After all, we are not in the Middle Ages.
Television foams over with dramas laid in immense general
hospitals of spotless cleanliness, high moral tone and nurses
with sharp breasts. The average viewer knows how to spot

one of these good-type hospitals at a glance and when he gets
his first glimpse of a typical private hospital, he knows—deep
down—that this cannot be one of those nice TV-style institutions. Instead, it's more of a backdrop for a horror show,
being dirty, old and crowded. A few have invested in a new
façade or even a new building. Most haven't. It would cut
into profits.

Why does anyone in the second half of the twentieth century patronize a private hospital? Its fees are as high as a good
voluntary hospital. True, it may be right around the corner
from home; most private hospitals are imbedded in the skin
of the residential neighborhood on which they prey. But
isn't it worth a ride in a cab or bus to get to a voluntary hospital? Oh, your doctor doesn't practice there? He practices at
the local private hospital? Ah. Light.

Let's dig a little deeper. If you can't really afford private-
hospital care, except by going into debt, why aren't you in a
public hospital? You've got a job? Ah. More light.

What have we here, then? Only the very rich and the very
poor get good medical care? Not quite. If by "good" care you
mean honest care, a public hospital will give it to a poor
person, true enough. It may not be terribly adequate, but it
is relatively free of deliberate lying, chicanery and useless
treatment for the sake of profit. For the privilege of being
treated with medical honesty, however, the poor person pays
not in money but in pride.

Pride is a commodity that can neither be bought nor sold.
It can only be lost. And every day, in all the many ways that
petty bureaucracies have at their disposal, clinic patients in
public hospitals are subjected to pride-destroying harassment
and humiliation.

The multitude of forms which must be filled out, the lines
in which one waits for everything, the brusque personal ques-
tioning, the open sneers, the general attitude of the help
which equates poverty with stupidity, the loud unwillingness

of clerks to help solve a patient's language differences, the constant efforts of lower-middle-class clerical help to remain one-up over patients, to inflate their own sadly squashed egos by reducing patients to ciphers devoid of dignity or pride— all these are the abuses of petty bureaucracy everywhere in the world. We may think of them as Old World traits, or abuses found in less democratic countries, but they are rife in our own and nowhere more nasty, more demeaning, more destructive of dignity, than in public hospitals where clerks wield a power over the aged and the poor that can amount to life or death.

To immigrants at the turn of the century, these hospitals were endured only until they could afford the care of a private doctor. To today's poor, some of them immigrants, many native Americans of the wrong color or age, the story is pretty much the same. Despite the great strides in medicine of this century, medical administration of public hospitals remains little improved.

Today's poor swear a silent oath as they endure the humiliation of public hospital administration: the moment they can afford it, they and their children will have a private doctor of their own and if, God forbid, they need hospitalization, it will be in a private institution.

This is their first mistake and the only one they need make in order to deliver themselves into the hands of the charlatans and cheats. By their deep-seated emotional need to recover pride, to escape second-class citizenship feelings created by the treatment they get in a public hospital, they run blindly from an uncomfortable frying pan into an all-consuming fire.

Who patronizes private hospitals? Poor people who aren't poor enough to qualify for public hospitals provide one source of business. Patients of doctors who cannot practice anywhere but at private hospitals constitute a primary source. Patients who will be getting operations that are difficult to get away with anywhere but in a private hospital make up a third group of customers. Another source of patients is among old people, set in their ways, who rely with blind devotion on the advice of the family doctor they have always used.

One group which provides the private hospital with steady business is made up of patients who have graduated cum laude in Health Insurance Fraud and can teach even the owners of the hospital a trick or two. These essentially larcenous people conspire with the hospital to give them whatever nonmedical care they require while arranging for their health insurance plan to pay for some treatment it normally covers. It is tempting to exonerate the hospital in such cases, so clear-cut is the patient's own initiative in the matter. But, of course, the fact remains that if the hospital were not eager to conspire to defraud the health insurance plan, the larcenous patient would be stopped in his tracks.

The mechanics of how all these innocent and not-so-innocent patients are variously preyed upon or catered to by the private hospital can best be seen by digging into the history of one such institution—one of the better ones, by the way, and certainly one of the most successful.

I'll call it Riverview Hospital and I'll locate it on Manhattan's West Side overlooking the Hudson River and the faraway delights of Weehawken.

Riverview is the shadow of one man, Sandy Hayes—Alexander R. Hayes, M.D.—by trade a general practitioner. In the early 1940's, shortly after he had earned his M.D., Sandy realized that the big money was in owning a hospital, not merely sending patients there. A vacant, roach-infested brownstone just off Riverside Drive was available for a ridiculously small cash down payment against a private mortgage. Hayes, his wife, his parents and his in-laws scraped together the necessary cash to buy the house and start its conversion to what they at first saw as a modest nursing home.

In those days, when the nation's economy was only just

climbing out of the Big Depression and war had already engulfed Europe, Sandy, his wife, his parents and his in-laws worked like dogs. The men knocked down partitions, built new ones, scraped and plastered. The women painted walls, mopped floors, and combed the *schmatta* pushcarts of Orchard Street for bargains in bed linen and mattresses. A typical Horatio Alger story, guaranteed to bring tears to your eyes, stood on the launching pad, waiting for the countdown.

Blast-off came when Sandy somehow got a 4-F deferment and became one of the few young doctors not hustled off to the war. Overnight, Sandy fell heir to a very extensive medical practice among the lower-middle-class families who lived in his neighborhood. While the doctors they normally used were serving in the armed forces, Sandy was enjoying the soft, easy life on the home front, working eighteen hours a day, drinking cold coffee out of paper cups, eating drugstore sandwiches and grabbing a few hours of sleep, constantly interrupted by emergency house calls throughout the night.

It was a genuinely hard time for Sandy Hayes and he performed a genuinely useful service to his community. He also got well paid for it. Shortly after V-J Day Sandy, his wife, his parents and his in-laws paid off the mortgage on the brownstone, bought the two adjoining ones outright, remodeled the entire complex as a five-story unit and still had enough money left over to take extended vacations in Miami Beach. They had earned the rest. In a way, all of them were war heroes.

Strange were the effects of the war on the practice of medicine. We all know of the tremendous advances in treatment and surgery developed more or less on the battlefields. Stranger still were war's effects on the memories of the patients many a GI doctor had left behind. Doctors returned to Manhattan's West Side to find that their patients were now permanently hooked on Sandy Hayes. "So hard-working," was the universal verdict; "so dedicated" was another; "so brilliant," a third.

"So entrenched" was the general feeling of some doctors returning to civilian life. But, true to our code of ethics, none of them lifted a finger to retrieve a former patient. A few, in fact, found a simple way to renew old acquaintance: they went to work for Sandy Hayes at Riverview Hospital.

Now began a period of transition for Riverview. Great events were taking place in the world of medicine. Health insurance became available. A new era was about to be ushered in.

It's my own opinion that Sandy was originally led astray by his patients, who recognized in him something none of us had seen, a broad streak of naked cupidity. Whoever took the initiative, the upper floor of Riverview Hospital, the one with the big windows facing south and west for the afternoon sun, was soon known throughout the West Side as Hayes' Country Club.

Elderly gents who held jobs and had health insurance became the Club's charter members. They would check in to Dr. Hayes' office for examination, well prepared with a solid list of symptoms that ranged from fainting spells and pains in the back to loss of "vitality" and hot flashes. The official diagnosis was whatever their health insurance would pay for that remotely resembled their symptoms. Regardless of their official disease, the course of treatment for these old codgers was remarkably the same from one to another. They were allowed to sleep late, lounge around the solarium in slippers and bathrobe, play pinochle and klabiash, drink countless glasses of tea, regale each other with unending stories of the good old days, and avoid their families like the plague. In short, their health insurance paid for a relaxing vacation.

Monday morning was the usual day of reckoning around Hayes' Country Club. Sandy would stride through the solarium, eyes swiveling left and right, finger pointing first to this luckless patient and then to that one. "You, out. You, there, you're much better. Go home. You in the corner, get dressed and leave. Grandpa, you with the cigar, beat it."

As soon as Sandy Hayes had cleared enough beds, the week's newcomers waiting in the receiving room were allowed to undress and join the club. Nurses and orderlies at Riverview Hospital used to marvel at the fact that, while most old-timers in bathrobes tended to look alike, Dr. Hayes had an unerring eye for the patients whose health insurance entitlement was about to run out.

Riverview continued to expand. From a nursing home it had become a rest home. Now, with the addition of a resident surgeon, some lab technicians and the engulfment of a neighboring brownstone in which Hayes set up an operating room, Riverview Hospital became a money-making investment far beyond the early dreams of Sandy, his wife, his parents and his in-laws.

What kind of surgeon would join Riverview? How good could its lab work be? And what about specialists to handle gynecological cases, bone and eye work, thoracic surgery, all the special cases a general surgeon shouldn't be asked to handle? How could Hayes afford 24-hour-a-day coverage?

Let's answer the questions in reverse order. Let's first find out who was available to cover Hayes around the clock. What M.D. could be persuaded to work through the post-midnight hours of the morning, sign his name to reports and records and handle emergency problems? Obviously a competent doctor who needed money. The only place you could find such an anomaly during the war was among refugee doctors without licenses. After the war, Sandy turned to the teaching hospitals, where third- fourth- and fifth-year residents were earning perhaps $200 a month, plus room and board, but were already fairly competent in their specialty. All it took to make such a man give up his bed at night and spend the tiny hours napping at a desk at Riverview Hospital while he covered the entire institution was a liberal amount of money, more than he earned as a resident, something on the order of $50 a night.

The fact that he had already put in a full day and was woozy with fatigue didn't make him a less competent doctor, did it? And besides, he was young, still in his twenties. He'd survive.

And so would his patients. This answers the question "Who handled all the special work at Riverview?" The answer is that there was no special work. Ninety-nine percent of the patients were not sick. Ninety-nine percent of the operations were needless.

Riverview was not in the doctoring business. It was solely in the business of making money.

How good was the lab work? No better than it needed to be. Sandy Hayes was clever enough—you may want to say compassionate enough—to know that really sick patients didn't belong in Riverview. He nearly always referred them to a good voluntary hospital. Where his danger lay was in the greed of an individual doctor who callously brought a really sick patient into Riverview.

A second danger lay in the sudden fluke, the unexpected accident, the undiagnosed problem through which a seemingly healthy patient abruptly went on the critical list. For the seriously ill patient, Riverview's lab work was completely inadequate. The hospital had no blood bank. True, it could get blood from a commercial supplier, just as it could rent certain emergency equipment if the need arose. But when you have a sudden fluke on your hands, speed is of the essence. It can and often does make the big difference. Waiting for an essential substance or piece of equipment to be delivered is not my idea of speed, nor that of most reputable hospitals, where every conceivable type of apparatus is kept on hand "just for emergencies."

Now we come to the question, "What kind of surgeon

would join Riverview?" First let me say that the particular surgeon who worked there was not a diplomate of the American Board of Surgery although he was a fellow of the American College of Surgeons. He was a general surgeon, which means he had tried almost every common kind of operation which can be done without special equipment or training. Open-heart surgery was beyond him and he knew it. So were many other modern techniques. It didn't matter. Ninety-nine percent of his work was useless, needless and without any reason except profit. Since he operated mainly on healthy people, his technique didn't need to be up-to-date. He didn't even have to be good. All that was important was that he wasn't too clumsy or too stupid. And, of course, that they kept him and the operating room clean.

Once again, however, Sandy Hayes faced certain dangers. It is possible for a doctor to perform his own surgery on his own patient at Riverview. He thus pockets two fees. This circumstance has led to some rather questionable situations and often some very dangerous ones, both for the patient and for the reputation and standing of Riverview.

I remember one such case in which I became involved. A doctor checked a patient into Riverview for a hysterectomy. The doctor was an impressive fellow, the possessor of a luxuriant black beard, heavy horn-rimmed spectacles and a wispy assistant who lighted his cigarettes for him.

With few, if any, misgivings, Hayes allowed the doctor to set up his patient. The operating room was reserved for 1 P.M. A hysterectomy, under normal conditions, is a rather simple operation. It is usually performed by opening the abdominal wall and removing the uterus and other parts of the reproductive system as are deemed necessary, then sewing up the wall again. It can be performed without opening the abdominal wall, but this is a special technique not too many gynecologists know or use.

At 1 P.M. the bearded surgeon, his slight assistant and his

patient foregathered in the operating room. At 2:00 the anesthetist ducked out of the room—strictly against the rules—
and placed a hurry-up call to Hayes in his office. Masked and
gowned, Sandy Hayes sidled into the operating room and
found that what the anesthetist had told him was substantially
correct.

The patient had now been on the table for 75 minutes.
In that time the bearded surgeon and his assistant had accidentally punctured her lower intestine in two different places
and had repaired the holes with a few casual stitches. They
had not yet begun to work on her tubes or uterus. As Hayes
watched and the clock ran on, they proceeded to tear a small
hole in the wall of her bladder, which they then took four
stitches to repair. Hayes stole out of the room to the telephone. He first asked for one of the fifth-year resident gynecologists at the hospital where I practice and teach. Finding
none available with whom he had done business, he asked
for me and quickly sketched in the outlines of the situation.
I got in my car.

By the time I, too, was scrubbed, gowned and ready to
enter the operating room, the clock showed 4 P.M. The patient
had been under anesthesia for three hours. I was ceremoni-
ously introduced to the beard and his assistant. We mumbled
through our masks. I examined the open patient. During the
time it had taken me to reach the hospital the visiting butchers
had hacked off several nonessential bits of tissue without coming to grips with what they were supposed to be doing, an
operation that in most cases lasts an hour. I nodded sagely
and began stitching shut the wall of the abdomen.

"But Doctor . . ." the bearded surgeon remonstrated.

"This patient," I announced, "has had enough surgery for
one day."

Later examination showed that no physical reason existed
for performing a hysterectomy. But the bearded doctor had
so convinced his patient she had malignant tumors that she

agreed to the operation. Slightly more than intrigued by a gynecologist-surgeon who couldn't locate and remove the womb and its trappings, I checked the professional qualifications of the visitor and learned, as I had suspected, that he had graduated with an M.D. from a small upstate medical college and had been perfectly content, down through the years, to refer his surgery to another man for the usual share. Something had happened between them. Perhaps the bearded one believed he deserved a larger share. At any rate they fell out and the hirsute charlatan decided to try his hand with the scalpel.

An out-and-out faker like the Bearded Butcher is always a problem to an anything-goes hospital like Riverview. But the vast majority of abuses within its walls are not the gross kind that stink so badly the world soon learns of them. Instead they are the small, petty, day-to-day routine abuses which everyone learns to accept and live with, perhaps in the manner prescribed by Zola when he suggested that to swallow some of the corruption of his own era one should, upon rising each morning, first swallow a toad.

It is this what-*me*-worry? attitude, this if-I-don't-do-it-somebody-else-will philosophy, this I'm-only-doing-what-the-patients-really-want rationalization that sustains Riverview Hospital's general surgeon during those few nights of the year when, conceivably, he may suffer from insomnia and the nagging questions of a moribund conscience.

His style of life, I should point out, makes it easy to forgive himself a few daily transgressions on decency and morality. His house in a fashionable suburb cost him about $150,000 and, although he didn't pay cash for it, he could have. He has a lovely wife, not the one who sweated out the lean years with him, but a svelte number he picked up later in life. By his first wife he has three lovely children he sees four times a year for a weekend each. By his second wife he has no children of his own; instead he has her three by two former marriages. Each of the six youngsters has a trust fund settled on his or her head, irrevocable in every case. Both wives have similar, but much larger, arrangements. In a rather garish three-room apartment in the East Seventies, his mistress has a silver Yorkshire and a charge account at Saks'. In other words, this man is drinking deeply of all the heady goodies American life can offer. True, he is paying rather stiffly for the goodies, but paying stiffly is part of success. How would you know you'd arrived if you weren't paying stiffly?

Whatever other goodies Riverview's surgeon is buying—automobiles, vacations, summer homes and the like—go a long way toward stilling any subversive, nasty little middle-of-the-night voices that repeat and repeat in his ear.

How does it feel, they ask, to lay a razor-sharp scalpel across the skin of a woman's abdomen, see the line of dark red blood rill up, slice through to the secret organs beneath, pretend to do something inside for a few moments to make everything legitimate, then sew her up again with a scar she and her lovers will wince at for the rest of her life?

How does it feel, they demand, to do all that, running the risk of infection, shock, pulmonary troubles and the like, and for no legitimate reason?

How does it feel, they persist, to do all that and then lie about it for money?

How does it feel to endanger life needlessly for money?

If the surgeon bothers to answer the questions of his conscience, he probably trots out a variety of excuses ranging from the particular to the sublime.

If I don't perform these "nothing" operations, he can say, someone else will. Since I am a pretty good surgeon, the patient is safer with me than with some butcher.

In the last analysis, who am I hurting? Health insurance pays the bills, the G.P. and I get our money, the hospital staff gets paid and the patient has a conversation piece for a few months.

Why all the heavy drama, he can ask, about what amounts to mere peanuts? Everywhere you look people are getting away with millions and lying about it. The newspapers print the lies and everybody nods happily and goes back to sleep. Why pick on me?

Endanger life for money? I'm not the only one doing it, he can protest. Read the headlines once in a while and wake up to what's happening in the world. Money is the name of the game. Play it or get off the earth.

Let's tiptoe out of the surgeon's office now while the last of these homilies reverberates with a tinny kind of truth in our ears. Sometimes even a charlatan gets too close to reality for comfort.

Let's, instead, consider how an entire hospital can get swept up in the tempo of corruption, the routine of it, to the point where dozens of perfectly ordinary citizens—not a crook in a carload—have created among themselves what amounts to a conspiracy of silence in which every one from Dr. Sandy Hayes, the owner, to Jesus Muñoz, who carries out the garbage, is involved in covering up for each other.

Is it really that bad? After all, what are they covering up besides some petty thievery? And all of them aren't involved that intimately, are they? Does Jesus Muñoz know what goes on when the surgeon cuts through in Mrs. Y's abdominal wall? Does Nurse Flannery actually know, when the record says a suspension was done, that the tubes were also tied at the same time? Does Anesthetist Prystalski understand that there was no real reason even to perform a suspension? How can I include all these people in a sweeping charge of conspiracy? How, for that matter, can Sandy Hayes or anybody else hold together an airtight, leakproof conspiracy year after year after year? Watch.

We're in the operating room at Riverview Hospital and the light is pouring down by the hundreds of candlepower from a new fluorescent ceiling fixture Sandy had installed last year. Ever alert to window dressing, Sandy realized that the last thing a patient sees before going under anesthesia is the ceiling fixture. Make it big, modern and expensive-looking.

Let's examine two different dramas that take place under those cool, utterly merciless lights. Although in the first instance the Riverview staff is guilty and, in the second, innocent, both stories illustrate the technique of conspiracy among perfectly normal people, none really a criminal, most just as average as average can be.

> SURGEON: (closing patient's abdomen after an unnecessary removal of a healthy uterus) Her color's bad.
> ANESTHETIST: We transfused her already.
> SURGEON: Get Sandy Hayes in here . . . fast.

By the time Sandy is gowned and masked, the patient has died on the operating table. Now Hayes, the surgeon and the anesthetist try to determine cause of death. The symptoms point a certain way.

> HAYES: Get her blood typed again. Do a re-crossmatch.

Ten minutes later the truth is clear. Whether through a technician's error, a clerical error in record-keeping or in labeling a bottle, the patient, Mrs. Y, has been given Type B blood when her own blood is Type A.

> HAYES: (A general under fire) Harry, get on the phone fast. Have the husband brought up. Make him sign a permit for an autopsy. Move! George, get her ready for an autopsy. Call Petersen and have him start cutting the second the husband signs.
> SURGEON: (subtly) What's Pete looking for?
> HAYES: (without a moment's hesitation) Fibroid uterus and massive pulmonary embolus.

If for no other reason, Hayes deserves his success because of the impressive manner in which his brain works under extreme tension. The fibroid uterus, of course, justifies the hysterectomy and the embolus substantiates the cause of death. Two cover-ups in one autopsy are thus achieved. If done properly and quickly, no one will ever know that there was no reason except greed for the original operation and no reason but stupidity or carelessness for the murder of Mrs. Y by giving her the wrong type of blood.

Drama Number Two.

> SURGEON: (*closing patient's abdomen after tying off her fallopian tubes, the operation being written up in the records as a suspension or appendectomy*) She looks pretty good to me.
>
> ANESTHETIST: Doing fine.

The next morning, recovering nicely, the patient, Mrs. Y, is urged to get up off the bed and take a few steps. She does and dies almost immediately. Sandy Hayes is instantly summoned. He surveys her as she lies on the bed.

> HAYES: Get a permit for an autopsy. Get Petersen in here fast. I'll help him with the job.

As the pathologist—who moonlights at Riverview—and Sandy Hayes explore the body of Mrs. Y they quickly learn that the cause of death was, indeed, a massive pulmonary embolus. Even with the best of care these things happen. Nothing the Riverview staff did, or neglected to do, caused the embolus.

But Sandy's still very much on the spot. The tubes show ligations. The record shows a "suspension." So he suggests to the pathologist that in the course of examining all of Mrs. Y's organs the tubes be snipped off and discarded. He also suggests that in this area of the body a number of blood vessels be severed, as if accidentally. Later, when the undertaker does his job, the cut vessels will make sure the embalming fluid isn't effectively spread throughout this area. Within a few weeks after burial, an exhumation and a subsequent autopsy will only find putrefaction.

Let's analyze what we have seen in terms of whether or not a conscious conspiracy exists. First of all, does everyone at Riverview know what really happened? Do all the nurses and orderlies and clerks, for example, understand that the wrong blood killed Mrs. Y? That a fake embolus was created as a cover story? Yes, they know, and for a very good reason.

They know one or more of them is the real murderer who actually misfiled Mrs. Y's blood-typing data, or took it down wrong, or mislabeled a bottle of blood, or didn't read the label carefully, or something. They also know that even if the death can be explained as simple carelessness and not traced back to any one individual, nothing about Riverview can stand the blinding light of day an investigation would throw on it. They may not know exactly what hanky-panky is committed, not by name and number, but they do know that "plenty's going on." How? The salaries give them a clue.

Hayes has been rather cunning about salaries. He pays more than any public or voluntary hospital can afford, but not that much more. There may be a 15 percent differential, enough to do the trick, not enough to stick out like a sore thumb. The extra money buys silence and loyalty. But it isn't so much extra that it starts to get the staff frightened about what they're doing. Clever.

Nevertheless, they're sure the bonus salaries are for winking at hanky-panky and they may even have suspected by now that some of it is related to sterilization or other "special" operations or to unnecessary surgery done solely for money. Even then there's nothing to worry about. Sterilization isn't illegal. It isn't paid for by any health insurance plan, but it's quite legal. Of course, entering it in the records as a suspension or some other innocuous operation is not so legal. It's fraud.

Obviously the pathologist saved a whole slew of jobs by

finding an embolus and a fibroid uterus in one case and by destroying the tubes in the other. Question: where did the fake tissue come from? Answer: what difference does it make? By the time this case has been worked up for the records, bona fide sections of tissue will be available for inspection.

Shocking stuff. Who can believe doctors would go to such lengths to cover up a simple mistake in a blood transfusion? But, it's not the original fatal mistake they hustle so hard to camouflage. It is the entire Riverview way of life, complete with eight trust funds, lengthy Southern vacations, opulent homes, overupholstered mistresses, the works. The goodies. The American Dream.

Mrs. Y. is dead. Telling the truth about why she died won't bring her back to life for her family. Telling the truth only destroys Riverview's ability to produce, over the years, millions of dollars for its owners and slightly less for its leading lights. So the truth remains untold. Instead, a conspiracy of silence, strong as steel, is forged. With the passing of time, more emergencies arise, more mistakes are made. The conspiracy is tested again. It holds firm because in addition to the other good reasons for silence there is now an even better one: accessory to several prior crimes. Interlocking guilts, interdependent greeds—these are the miracle adhesives that hold Riverview together against the world.

I have picked Riverview Hospital to anatomize for several reasons. The way it came into being is consistent with the highest attributes of American life: hard work, family loyalty, service to the community. More to the point, I chose Riverview because, as I warned you, it is among the best of the private hospitals. Its physical plant is impeccable, what there is of it. The tiled walls and floors are spotlessly maintained. It hires only the most brilliant young residents for moonlight coverage. Its house surgeon is very good and still in the prime of his powers; his fingers do not shake as yet, nor does his

glance waver. Sandy Hayes himself is a bright, friendly, pleasant, go-getting individual. You would be pleased to have him
move in next door to you. If his son proposed marriage to
your daughter you would arrange for the wedding with a high
heart.

Riverview's neighborhood is no longer the same. Middle-
class families no longer dominate the area. Along Broadway
and the side streets Puerto Rican families try to gain a foot-
hold in New York. Young marrieds move in and out of Riverside Drive, wheel their babies through the Park. Along West
End Avenue, the multi-room apartments are still rent-con-
trolled and only here does the flavor of the old neighborhood
remain unchanged in some respects.

But very little else changes for Riverview. In a city the size
of New York, with its hundreds of neighborhood G.P.'s and
specialists, there will always be a place for tolerant, permissive hospitals like Riverview, where anything goes.

Dr. Jekyll and Dr. Hyde

Only rarely does the average person get a peek behind the
façade that hides most medical corruption from public view.
Harvey Hamburg, M.D., provided one of those rare moments.

Harvey was not a sin-steeped charlatan in the accepted sense
of the word. Harvey was, if anything, a moderately honest
man. It was this, more than anything else, that finally exposed
him to public scorn. Honesty was his undoing.

Harvey Hamburg was an internist. This medical specialty
is not always fully understood by laymen, or by some doctors,
for that matter. Laymen tend to confuse the internist with the
G.P. Actually, having completed all the academic and hospital
work required of a G.P., the internist then takes a two- or

three-year residency in internal medicine. He works in the hospital, gaining special knowledge of those ailments—typically, of the heart, lungs and stomach—which are usually treated without surgery but may require surgery later.

Where the specialty tends to get further confused is that there are internists who deal solely with the heart or the stomach, for example. They are specialists, so to speak, with a special subspecialty.

Harvey Hamburg's specialty was diabetes. He knew as much about this disease as anyone else and considerably more than most. He gained this knowledge by study and by treating as many cases of diabetes as he could get. In order to come in contact with as many cases as possible, Harvey devoted much of his time to working in a public hospital in Queens and in a fairly good voluntary hospital in Brooklyn. In both institutions he treated patients, taught interns and residents, consulted on cases, was called in for diagnosis and other medical matters.

Still and all, Harvey Hamburg was starving.

I use the term hyperbolically. Harvey obviously knew where his next meal was coming from and could probably be counted on to pay his bills within, say, a liberal six months. But compared to other internists, Harvey was not making a decent living.

One trouble with Harvey lay in the specialty he had chosen. Internal medicine is a specialty like any other and its practitioners depend on referrals from other doctors, mainly G.P.'s. If you are a surgeon, G.P.'s must refer cases to you. You may induce them to do more of it by paying sub-rosa kickbacks. But the fact remains that you are in an entirely different business from a G.P., so to speak, and he must come to you. The internist's work is close enough to that of a G.P. for the latter to resist referring patients. The G.P. thinks to himself: "Why give a patient the idea that there's a certain kind of doctor who's like a G.P., only better? When I refer

patients, it's got to be to someone with a recognizably different racket than mine. Or to unload a problem case."

Thus, to begin with, Harvey Hamburg began his life as a
specialist with at least one strike against him. The second
strike was his utter and abysmal lack of personal charm. He
could belong to every conceivable medical society, club and
log-rolling association, attend every dinner and outing and
theater party, but Harvey remained totally unmemorable.
People were completely underwhelmed by Harvey.

The third strike, and the one that kept sending Harvey
back to the dugout, was his honesty. Although corruption
may well be the most powerful link holding together many
medical communities, in Harvey's case his honesty was the
most important reason for his failure. Like the wallflower at
the fraternity house party, he remained utterly pure, his re-
sistance against temptation perfectly intact, because nobody
had tempted him.

Such was the situation when Harvey Hamburg came to
the attention of Sandy Hayes, owner of Riverview Hospital.

In what happened af , I do not mean to cast Sandy in
the role of Satan. He most emphatically did not connive to
bring about Harvey's fall from grace. All he wanted to exploit
was Harvey's innate thickheadedness, and at bargain rates.

Riverview Hospital needed a chief of medicine. This was
the man who served as an opposite number to the chief of
surgery. Both titles were somewhat illusionary since, in the
case of the chief of surgery, only "nothing" operations were
performed at Riverview, and in the case of the chief of medicine, virtually no really sick people were admitted to the
hospital.

Nevertheless, Sandy Hayes' old chief of medicine had died.
He needed someone to serve as a medical consultant, read
electrocardiograms and sign charts to substantiate fake insurance claims. Obviously, since this was more or less a
figurehead position, Hayes needed someone very corrupt or

very stupid. Since a corrupt man would have demanded a lot of money, Hayes chose Harvey Hamburg.

For a while, everything went very well for Harvey. He had a small practice of his own, which came to him through his voluntary hospital affiliation. He managed to keep his hand in at his subspecialty, diabetes. And at Riverview he also managed to eke out a tidy side income that brightened his financial picture considerably.

Since you have already met the dramatis personae of Riverview Hospital, you are well aware of the kinds of things that were going on within its walls. It may have been among the better, cleaner, more mannerly private hospitals. But it was, nevertheless, not in the healing business. Its sole concern was the separation of patients from their personal bankrolls or their health insurance entitlement.

It is thus proper to ask, how naïve could Harvey Hamburg be? We can admit he was thickheaded. But was he also deaf, dumb and blind? Did he not, in fact, quickly catch on to what he was really doing at Riverview?

There is, of course, no way of knowing the absolute truth about this, as about too many other things in life. I can tell you that Harvey spent only a few hours a week at Riverview. Sometimes several days might go by without his being there. It is possible, too, that since he saw very few patients, Harvey could conceivably not have known for a long while what was actually going on.

More likely, he was slow to understand what was happening and even slower to accept his role in the medical make-believe show. I like to think of Harvey Hamburg as pondering the problem for many months without seeing his own involvement, then catching a glimmer of it, rejecting it, being forced by logic to accept some responsibility and, eventually, after perhaps a year or more of thought, reaching the conclusion that he should pocket the money and say nothing.

If I am right about the decision he finally made, then it

was Harvey Hamburg's first consciously corrupt act. If I am wrong, it makes very little difference in what finally befell Harvey.

Let's put it this way: working for Sandy Hayes made Harvey, at the least, accessible to corruption. But it was his meeting with Max Marvin that finally opened the Gates of Hell for Harvey.

Max Marvin was everything Harvey was not. Max was slim, well-dressed, with an Ivy League drawl learned the hard way, by watching old college movies. Harvey was chubby, dumpy and always slightly damp with perspiration. He grossed about thirty thousand a year, now that he was "covering" at Riverview. Max Marvin rarely grossed less than eighty thousand. In a good year he would pull in twice that, every cent of it from poor people.

Max's operation was only a notch below Riverview Hospital and only a notch above the "blood doctor" racket. Max ran a private clinic. Poor people who might have their egos trampled to death in a public clinic while they got good, honest medical care preferred Max Marvin's clinic, where they were treated like human beings of some consequence and milked for every last cent they could beg from their relatives or steal from their health insurance.

Max's clinic was one of many feeder lines for Sandy Hayes' Riverview Hospital. It was a rare day that didn't see some patient arrive at Riverview with an imaginary ailment, diagnosed by Max Marvin as requiring hospitalization. Inevitably, Harvey Hamburg began to work with Max, albeit indirectly, whenever a chart needed to be signed.

I like to indulge my own rudimentary sense of dramatics by pinning the horns and the forked tail on Max Marvin. But, whereas he might well have been Harvey's Mephistopheles, by the time the two met, Harvey was well on his way to being Dr. Faustus. In other words, Max was eager for Harvey's soul and Harvey was dying to sell it.

Once again, I may be doing Harvey a disservice. It is quite possible he began his association with Max Marvin under the most innocent circumstances. Max may have suggested that he needed an internist to do some of the same things at his clinic that Harvey was already doing at Riverview Hospital. Harvey may have seen a way of picking up some spare change now and then. Handily enough, Max Marvin's clinic was only a few blocks away from Riverview.

In any event, Harvey was soon making nearly as much from the clinic as from the hospital. Things were definitely looking up.

Whereas it is somewhat conceivable that Harvey could not have known, entirely, what was going on at Riverview, it is beyond credence to think he was unaware of Max Marvin's methods.

The clinic was a grind operation. It depended on sheer numbers. Its usual treatment was a pill or a shot. If Marvin spent more than a minute or two per patient he was operating at a loss. The entire routine was under the supervision of nurses who were well paid for their combined jobs as orderlies, monitors, policemen and hypodermic wielders. With the entire clinic geared to a high-volume, low-integrity pitch, no one but the patients could possibly be taken in by any lip service to the ideals of healing.

So Harvey Hamburg's fall from innocence must have happened rather quickly. Within a year's time, Max Marvin was blithely taking off on a one-month vacation, secure in the knowledge that he could turn over his work to a qualified— indeed a highly qualified—M.D. who, under the guidance of the nurses, would cope with the grind while Max invited his soul in various watering places.

Let's take a fast look at a day in the life of Harvey Hamburg. Up at 6. Rounds at the public hospital. Rounds at the voluntary hospital. Clinic at 10. Lunch at noon. Riverview at 2. Clinic again. Private patients three times a week in his own office at night. His gross income was now up past about forty-five thousand a year. He joined a country club.

Let's be fair to Harvey. Let's say he tried his best to maintain integrity up and down the line. I know he did in his public and voluntary hospital affiliations. I believe he did in his private practice, where he had the time to take a complete history, perform careful examinations, reach a prudent diagnosis and course of treatment.

But by becoming a cog in the clinic machinery designed by Max Marvin, Harvey surrendered integrity by the bucketful. Because he knew better, his sin was the greater. And, when it finally became public, it was almost as if, his sin being greater, his fall was all the harder.

Downfall arrived in the form of a small boy aged six with a very sore throat.

Now, Harvey was no pediatrician. Neither, for that matter, was he a surgeon, and yet in the normal course of the clinic day he was called on to perform minor surgery. He did whatever had to be done, regardless of the fact that he was not trained to do it. That was the pattern of the clinic. You conformed to the pattern or you looked elsewhere for money.

Harvey glanced down the boy's throat and prescribed 300,000 units of penicillin. This boy had walked into his view less than a minute before. He was a medical cipher to Harvey, nothing but a reported symptom with an inflamed throat to back it up.

A nurse injected 300,000 units of penicillin. Within two minutes the boy was dead.

Violent allergic reactions to penicillin still occur, even at this late date. They are extremely rare nowadays. Doctors are leery of giving indicated injections of penicillin unless they know something about the patient's history. Only if he has proved able to take penicillin without an allergic reaction, will a patient get more of it, should his condition warrant.

In his private practice, Harvey Hamburg was careful to check rather thoroughly into this and other aspects of his patient's history.

The clinic operation, of course, simply budgeted no time at all for such frills. It provided barely enough time for the most superficial examination. Under those circumstances, any careful doctor would tell you—Harvey himself would tell you—it was only a matter of time before something happened very much like what actually did happen.

The parents, though poor, managed to reach out for justice. They enlisted the support of an afternoon paper, which went after Harvey and the clinic with such gusto that Max Marvin cut short his vacation and hurried back from Acapulco in time to read it and weep.

For Max the exposé was bothersome indeed. Volume at the clinic fell off sharply. Max didn't know whether to change the name or move the location. Or both. But time answered the question for him. Within a few weeks the whole thing blew over. People began returning to the clinic. After all, people did die, didn't they? Even children. It was part of life, wasn't it? Volume rose. Business returned to normal.

For Harvey Hamburg the sudden exposure of his corruption was terribly embarrassing. Colleagues at the voluntary hospital and the public hospital gave him funny looks. A few came right out and wondered aloud what the hell he'd been doing in that clinic, anyway—a man with his background. None of them was man enough to admit that business failure had driven Harvey to corruption. Each took a mealymouthed, holier-than-thou tone that converted Harvey from a fellow sinner to a sacrificial burnt offering.

At the country club, matters grew especially embarrassing because the doctor-members gossiped with the laymen-members at every opportunity, using Harvey's disgrace as a way of reflecting glory and integrity on themselves.

But the well-to-do are not that different from the poor in

the length of their memories. Eventually the scandal died down. Harvey's plodding good qualities were recalled. After all, by sheer dint of perseverance and remaining alive, he did know a lot about diabetes, didn't he?

Today, Harvey has turned his back on obvious corruption. He still works as a figurehead for Sandy Hayes at Riverview Hospital. A man has to eat. But he has nothing to do with Max Marvin and will, in fact, cross the street to avoid saying hello to him.

My Own Personal, Private Doctor

On Chicago's South Side, in the Hyde Park area around the University of Chicago with its excellent Billings medical center, there is a lovely stretch of greensward, the Midway, a kind of broad mall that reaches from the edge of Lake Michigan on west to the small, attractive Washington Park. The neighborhood north of the mall and east of the park is the proper province of the University, with its many thousands of students, its immense research facilities, and the maternity and children's hospitals attached to Billings. West of the park and south of the mall lie several depressed areas once the Irish-Polish neighborhoods celebrated in *Studs Lonigan*, now heavily Negro in population.

On the "right" side of the line, well within the University's area, stands an apartment building, one of many five- and six-story structures put up just before the Great Depression. It fronts on the mall and its view of various University hospitals, dormitories and other buildings is a good one. On the ground floor of this building, a few yards away from the recessed entry, is a door leading directly to the street. Next to the

door is a very discreet bronze plaque on which raised letters
spell out A. B. Farewell, M.D.

In the constant struggle of poor people everywhere to rise
up out of poverty, the role of doctors like Farewell provide
some interesting insights.

Farewell himself is a hard-working man. Now in his early
sixties, he remains skinny and spry through hard work. His
office suite includes two waiting rooms, a tiny clerical office
for his receptionist-bookkeeper, two examining rooms and a
hall-like dispensary that was once, perhaps, a corridor from
kitchen to dining room. He has done little to change the
apartment-like qualities of the suite, except for painting the
examining rooms white.

The only other non-apartment characteristic of the suite
is the presence in every corner, along every wall, in every
alcove, nook and cranny of chairs. There are literally dozens
of chairs throughout the suite, in addition, of course, to a
number of sofas and benches. The tremendous seating capacity of Farewell's office suite gives us our first clue to the business he's in.

Clue Number Two: the long dispensary. From floor to ceiling, the yards of shelves are stocked with bottles and boxes of
drugs, proprietary medicines and other pharmaceuticals. Let's
look at the labels. The manufacturers of the drugs are a vir-
tual Who's Who of anonymity. If it is possible to stock a
dispensary with literally tens of thousands of dollar's worth
of supplies and not once buy a pill bearing the recognizable
name of a major pharmaceutical concern, Farewell has turned
the trick. On closer inspection, we find that many of these
nonentity drug companies are based outside the U. S. in
places like Mexico and Japan. This, in itself, means nothing,
but does attest to the low cost of the drugs. And, of course,
this is the basic reason for the no-name situation. Farewell
buys supplies, at wholesale, much less expensively than the
corner druggist buys his name-brand pharmaceuticals.

Clue Number Three: location. Farewell's office is in a "good," *i.e.*, white, neighborhood with overtones of strong medical stature. He's literally in the shadow of Billings Hospital, literally under the wing of the august University of Chicago and its medical school. At the same time, you can actually walk to his office from the nearby "bad," *i.e.*, Negro neighborhoods. The Cottage Grove bus runs only a block or two from his door. So does the 55th Street line.

Clue Number Four: number of patients. Let's walk in on Farewell around noontime. Sure enough, he's sitting behind his desk eating the skimpy roast beef sandwich on rye bread he brought from home this morning. A percolator on the hot-plate behind his desk provides his cup of coffee. He's deeply engrossed in his lunchtime reading, hunched over the *Tribune*'s N. Y. Stock Exchange listings. Farewell's portfolio, at the moment, is heavily invested in commons. Meanwhile, in the two waiting rooms, the halls, the alcoves, nooks and crannies, patients are waiting.

This is the final clue to Farewell's business, the 10 to 15 patients who are always to be found waiting in his anterooms. Farewell doesn't keep them there out of meanness. As a matter of fact, Farewell isn't entirely responsible for putting them in the position of having to wait for him. His patients have no one to blame but themselves and the society that molds their beliefs for having to sit many long hours, waiting for the privilege of being treated by Farewell, their own personal, private doctor.

The business Farewell is in, of course, is the business of providing the semblance of private medical care for patients who have enough money—barely enough—to lift themselves up out of free clinic care.

But see how carefully Farewell has both stage-managed the scene and built into it certain guarantees that he will make a good profit even out of essentially poor patients. His location, carefully chosen, confers maximum status on his patients.

Being on the border of a ghetto, Farewell does not force his patients to travel for many miles through well-to-do neighborhoods. His location thus has both prestige and convenience. In the minds of his patients—although he has carefully avoided putting it there in so many words—is the sincere conviction that Farewell is either connected with the immense medical complex of the University or, perhaps, even sanctioned by it as a kind of official or semi-hemi-demi-official adjunct. Otherwise why would they let him have his office that close?

So much for status and convenience. Now for profit. The base of Farewell's profit structure is low overhead. In a neighborhood of students and young married families, his landlord considers himself lucky to be able to lease an apartment that big. Farewell's rent is low. His remodeling costs were even lower. He has a nurse and a receptionist, thus keeping salary costs low. On this base he erects a profit structure in much the same manner as any other G.P.: unnecessary treatment for nonexistent ailments, overextended treatment for existing ailments, exaggeration of small complaints into major medical problems, careful spacing out of fee payments (charging $5 a week for one year is the same as charging $260 one time, only better because Farewell's patients can manage to find $5 a week, in cash), a judicious use of fear psychology in hinting at cancer or syphilis, and rather lucrative relationships with a number of specialists.

But Farewell has erected something extra on this profit structure, his dispensary. Instead of writing prescriptions which then walk out of his life forever, to enrich some ghetto druggist with whom he has no business relationship, Farewell prescribes and fills his own prescriptions. That is, he prescribes medication he knows to be in his dispensary and avoids prescribing medication which would require a pharmacist to compound out of separate ingredients.

The markup on Farewell's own pharmaceuticals, as we

have seen, must be enormous. While it is true that most drugs have a fairly long bottle life, the pharmaceuticals bought at a reputable drugstore are usually fairly fresh. No one, probably including Farewell, knows how long some of his drugs have rested on the shelves of his dispensary or whether, indeed, they were old when he bought them at bargain prices. The combination of buying off-brand, foreign and outdated pharmaceuticals gives Farewell's dispensary a basis on which to charge whatever the traffic will bear for dispensing drugs. Farewell resists temptation, usually, and rarely overcharges his patients. He even believes in free missionary work: on occasion he will dispense a pill or two absolutely free of charge. These are free drug-company samples, of course. Farewell is not the darling of the pharmaceutical-house detail men, despite the volume of business he does. They're aware of the fact that Farewell is less a potential customer than a competitor of theirs. Be that as it may, Farewell will occasionally give away a few capsules of something. If it works, you may be sure he will find a cheap substitute for it in his dispensary shelves and sell it by the bottle on the patient's next visit.

Let's sum up Farewell's operation by saying that he provides all of the disadvantages of public clinic practice with none of the advantages of free care. Consider for a moment: in the clinics patients wait for hours before getting to see a doctor for a few precious moments. The same is true of Farewell's patients, except that they pay for the privilege.

Why do they?

Why do they buy, for about $5 a visit and whatever the pharmaceuticals cost, the right to cool their heels in the waiting room? Why have they turned their backs on the honest medical care and free pharmaceuticals of the public hospital and clinic?

Part of the answer lies in the fact that they have achieved new, higher status by being able to afford their own personal, private doctor, a man who is vaguely associated with the University hospitals and whose office is in a nice part of town, but not too hard to get to.

Part of the answer is found in their treatment by Farewell and his staff. They are always addressed as Mr. or Mrs. or Miss. They get a smile. They have magazines to look at in the waiting room. It's air-conditioned. It resembles a nice apartment. Dr. Farewell remembers them by name. They're not just another walking body to him. To their own personal, private doctor each of them is an individual human being.

Part of the answer, too, is the distrust poor people have of free treatment. Not only does it smack of dehumanization and prying into personal matters, but it also runs counter to certain ingrained truths: "for nothing you get nothing," "free advice is worth just what you paid for it," "why should anyone do me a favor?" and "what's the catch?" Underlying these concepts, finally, is the basic pride of people and their often fierce determination to "take care of themselves" without anyone's help. Hiring your own personal, private doctor is one of the fundamental ways you assert your freedom from dependency on others.

Farewell provides the trappings of private practice. His patients do the rest . . . to themselves.

Skin Game

Dermatology is by no means an exact science. Neither is any other part of medicine, for that matter, but dermatology seems to have such a large element of emotional causation to it that a good dermatologist must, I think, be almost as adept at psychology.

About the best dermatologist of my acquaintance is Alfred Corwin. He has all the right diplomas and has passed all the proper boards. He teaches dermatology and he carries on one of the most extensive practices in Chicago. One of the most lucrative, too.

Although Al Corwin normally charges $25 for a simple consultation visit, all therapy is charged for additionally, and my, but Al's patients need an awful lot of therapy. In addition to X-ray series, they require scraping, freezing, planning, cutting, drying and draining. Al is known for his ability to escalate a simple consultation into a series of visits that bring him $25 a week for several years. And it even helps the patient's skin, too.

For several years I shared an office suite with Al Corwin. Al not only leased the suite but also his wife served as the receptionist-nurse for all of his subtenants, including me. We had a rudimentary kind of lab off the examining room where we could run a few tests when the occasion arose. It was actually more of a storeroom.

I was in it one day as Al entered from his consulting room. Through the doorway I could see a young fellow in his twenties seated on the table stripped to the waist. He wore thick-soled workingman's shoes with high, untanned uppers. At the moment, Al was preparing to do away with a growth of some kind on the young man's face. Not being too familiar with the process, I watched him desiccate the growth in about a minute's time, using a needle, then put the patient in another room to undergo a brief session of X-ray therapy which the nurse (Mrs. Corwin) supervised while Al ushered in the next patient.

By accident I had finished for the day and was crossing the patient's waiting room on my way out of the office when the young man, now fully clothed in a blue denim workshirt and wool jacket, stopped by the reception desk to pay what he owed.

As if at a signal—which, for all I know, there may have been—Al Corwin appeared in the doorway of his consulting room and clapped his arm around the young man's shoulder.

"Dotty," he told the receptionist-nurse-X-ray-therapist-wife, "we don't want to charge this young man our regular fee. He works hard for a dollar, Dotty. Let's charge him, oh, say, $35 for the consultation, $15 for the desiccation and $10 for the X-rays."

I stood there watching the look of real pleasure on Al Corwin's face as he beamed paternally at the young man. Then I saw the doglike look of gratitude on the patient's face. Then I left ... hurriedly.

As I said, Al Corwin was good. He was good enough that he occasionally got a fairly well-known person passing through town, referred to him for some special dermatological work, usually surgical in nature. There was a slight stir this one day among the mothers and their acne-ridden daughters who sat patiently in the waiting room. A gentleman had entered whom even I recognized as a Somebody. In those days he was an actor of some merit who had already drawn favorable attention in a number of successful stage productions. But what stirred the teen-agers' hearts was the fact that his first film had been a smash success and he was getting the big buildup. Part of it included the removal of a growth on his cheek so similar to the one Al Corwin had removed from the young workingman that it might have been a twin.

The treatment was almost identical, too: a minute's work with a needle and a touch of X-ray. But this time the patient didn't have to apply to the receptionist for his bill. Al Corwin told him not to worry, he'd be billed by mail. He was, for $750.

Normally, with a growth that small, a patient would probably not return again. But the actor did, probably within a few hours of receiving Al's bill. He stalked through the waiting room and confronted Al at his desk.

"I'm leaving for the Coast," he said in firm, resonant, carrying tones produced properly from the diaphragm.

"Wonderful," Al said.

"I'll give you my address out there," the actor stated with perfect enunciation, and did so.

"Thank you," said Al.

"That's where your lawyer can send the summons," announced the actor ringingly. "Because if you think I have any intention of paying your bill you are out of your skull. You will have to sue me to get a single penny."

With which he stalked right out again, out of the office and out of Al's life. I hated to see him go. He was absolutely the only patient who had ever beaten Al Corwin out of a cent, let alone $750.

And if there be an opportunity of serving one who is a stranger in financial straits, give full assistance to all such. For where there is love of man, there is also love of the art.

—from the Precepts of Hippocrates

Bad Blood

You will find them on the finest golf courses around Chicago and New York. Their homes are in the lovelier suburbs. Their wives are photographed with other ladies to publicize charitable causes in the women's pages of the *Trib,* where pictures of their daughters mark engagements and weddings. When the average layman learns that they are doctors he pictures large Sheridan Road office suites, nurses in starched linens, society patients, film stars, a chauffeur-driven Rolls-Royce Silver Cloud to whisk him on his rounds, gay evenings in the company of homosexual artists, film-makers and symphony conductors, the works.

But reality is different. They tend to drive Fords or Chevvies to work because their cars aren't supposed to attract attention. They make no house calls. Their second-floor offices lie along South State Street and other clogged cross-arteries of Chicago's Harlem. Their nurses are harassed, overworked and grumpy. Their patients are day laborers, truck helpers, garment center cart pushers, night janitors, delivery boys, filling station attendants, doormen, all the marginal, low-paying but garnisheeable jobs which Negroes and Puerto Ricans fill in the Big City.

These doctors see film stars only on the screen and homosexual artists only in society columns. They live in Glencoe and prey on the poor.

They are bad blood doctors.

Let's watch one at work. But let's shift the scene to New York, just for security's sake.

It's 9:30 in the morning. Dr. Crain has been at his desk in his second-floor walkup off Lenox Avenue since 8:30. Now Patient Number Seven opens the door and walks in. Patient Number Seven is a tall, skinny Negro male; age, forty-two; occupation, clean-up man in a wholesale meat market on Washington Street down near the lower West Side docks.

From midnight to 8 A.M. he has been pushing a heavy iron dumpcart around the abattoir, a cart somewhat the same as that used by a street cleaner. He, too, has a shovel, but no broom. His job is to scoop up those heads, entrails and organs for which the New York public has not yet acquired a taste. He shovels these by-products of the meat-carving process into his cart in a surrealist mélange of blue-white intestines and dark red spleens, blind-eyed severed heads, lungs, udders, hooves, stomachs, rumens and the like.

He has been at this for eight hours with a half-hour break at 4 A.M. to eat lunch. He is now on his way home to a three-room flat on 121st Street which he shares with his wife, three children, sister-in-law and her child and his seventy-eight-year-old mother-in-law. He will sleep fitfully from about 10 A.M. to about 4 P.M., rise, eat and take the subway down to the Garment Center, where he will put in the hours from 5 P.M. till just before midnight cleaning an entire eight-story building on the corner of 36th Street. There are two dress manufacturers on each floor. He will remove the trash from sixteen small factory layouts, including butts, wastepaper, fabric trash and the like. He will light-mop all floors and, on Friday night, heavy-mop them. He will damp-cloth desk tops in the showrooms, replace paper in the toilets and squeegee glass entry doors to each showroom. At midnight he will make a dash south for the wholesale meat market job and the iron cart full of guts.

Now he sits down across from Dr. Crain and his eyelids droop slightly. His walk had been somewhat unsteady as he moved across the room, but once he's seated, he's all right.

"You look tired," Crain tells him.

"Um, you know it, Doc. And I get these shooting-kind pains here." He indicates the small of his back and the backs of his calves and thighs.

Crain's face looks very, very grave. He moves to the fluoroscope. This is a third-hand machine he bought after the war. It cost $25 because its Roentgen tube no longer emitted X-rays. Instead, a narrow greenish light and a buzzer have been installed just behind the fluorescing window that slides up and down. A heavyset nurse enters the room and helps the patient remove his mackinaw jacket and shirt. The nurse shoves the patient between the cold metal plate through which X-rays are supposed to come and the cold glass plate where his innards are about to reveal all. She lowers the shades and turns off the light. Dr. Crain has ostentatiously donned his lead apron. He grasps the timer-switch at the end of the long black electric wire, assumes a slight crouch before the face of the fluorescing window, squints his eyes and does a creditable imitation of a home plate umpire who is not going to let any strikes get through as balls, or vice versa.

The buzzer buzzes, the green light flickers and, in the eerie moment of waiting, Dr. Crain's face looks, if anything, even graver. He repeats the charade twice more, whips off his apron and calls for lights.

Now the patient is led back to the desk where his left thumb is swabbed with alcohol and pricked just deeply enough to emit one pearl of blood. Crain touches a glass microscope slide to the pearl and removes most of it as a red circle on the slide. This he places under an extremely large brass microscope, vintage 1890. He fiddles with the mirror, adjusts the stage, twiddles the objective and racks the tube up and down a few times. It does no harm since there are no lenses. "I was afraid of that," he mutters at last.

" 'Fraid of what?" the patient asks anxiously.

"Um. Yes." Crain removes the slide and hands it to the nurse. "Burn it," he orders. Then he does a rapid hand-washing routine at the nearby basin. Tension thickens.

Now he returns to the desk, sits down and fixes his patient, man-to-man, with a penetrating glance. "Let me guess," he says then. "You're a little more tired than usual lately. Right?"

"That's right."

"Harder to climb those stairs."

"The truth."

"Can't seem to get any good out of sleeping," Crain continues, "and sometimes you don't even get to sleep more than an hour or two."

The patient is wide-eyed. All this from looking at his innards and his blood? "What is it?" he asks. "What's wrong?"

Crain shakes his head sadly, chidingly, but with a faintly insinuating look in his eyes. "You know what you've got better 'n I do."

The patient is really bewildered now. "What is it?"

"You must know." The doctor leans closer. "It's, uh, well, let's call it . . . bad blood."

The patient recoils from the words. Sweat breaks out on his face. "How bad, Doc?"

"Not good." Slow smirk. Without using a word like syphilis, the implication is nevertheless strong, "You must've really cut out wide to get your blood in that kind of shape."

"Not me. I don't fool around."

"Maybe not now. But this could've been any time in the last ten years."

"No."

"Yes. You just never know." The doctor has been busily scribbling on a pad. Now, he tears off the sheet and hands it across to the patient. "I'm afraid it's shots for you."

"Will they help?"

"Only thing that will. Otherwise. . . ." Fatalistic shrug. "See the nurse on your way out and make the arrangements. Only don't let too much time go past. I can't guarantee the shots'll work if you don't start today and stick with them religiously."

Item: ten injections of saline solution administered sub-cutaneously by the nurse every morning for the next ten days, at $5 an injection—$50.

Item: a prescription for "blood pills" of the doctor's own formulation at $5 a dozen for two dozen—$10.

Item: original examination—$5.

Item: concluding examination—$5.

Item: fluoroscopy—$5.

Item: initial microscopic blood examination—$5.

Item: concluding blood examination—$5.

Total: $85, payable in ten equal installments of $8.50.

While the patient is signing contracts for this, Patient Number Eight is ushered into Dr. Crain's presence. Crain's glance slips sideways to the clock on the wall. He's maintaining his usual average of five to six patients an hour. Many are new to him, like the one he's just put on injections. A great many more are repeaters, like the man who sits before him now.

"Don't have none of that git-up-and-go no more," he tells Dr. Crain.

"Still got that job with the restaurant?"

Patient Number Eight starts work in the kitchen, peeling potatoes and chopping vegetables, at 7 A.M. He cleans dishes and silverware all day, mops up between breakfast and lunch, between lunch and dinner and after dinner, sweeps out, emp-ties garbage, unloads cartons. He gets two meals a day free and the time off between 3 and 6 P.M. He finishes work about 10 at night, sometimes earlier.

"I'm worried about that tiredness," Crain tells him. "Your blood must be in much worse shape than I thought."

Crain glances at the clock again. His mind is not on his work today. This evening he and his wife are hosts to a Sweet Sixteen party for their younger daughter at the country club. Everyone will be there. The Lincolns and Jaguars will line up along the curving drive and under the porte cochere. There will be a 12-piece orchestra and a three-man rock-and-roll group. The local newspaper is sending a photographer.

"More shots?" Patient Number Eight asks, thinking of how to pay for them.

"Definitely."

Money Matters

Although the unwritten law of fee-setting has always been to charge what the traffic will bear, I've occasionally run across some curious and often funny variations on the basic rule.

Perhaps the most peculiar variations can be found among "blood doctors" who prey on the poor. The manner in which they state their fees most closely parallels the style of other retail advertising directed at this market. Chicago stores like Goldblatt's, or New York emporiums like S. Klein's will blazon immense headlines that hint at a behind-the-scenes disaster which the public can take advantage of—FAMOUS-MAKE MANUFACTURER BANKRUPTCY! . . . *We've snapped these up at below wholesale cost . . . you snap them up at the lowest price in our history!* Another technique is the two-for-one price, another "we can't tell you the maker's name, but," and so on.

Harry Grief had actually missed his calling. Instead of operating a storefront clinic on North Rush Street in Chicago's Old Town, he would have been happier running a chain of distressed-merchandise dress shops. A general practitioner, Harry did the best he could with the raw material at hand.

While individual doctors can't advertise, private clinics can and do distribute certain forms of advertising disguised as public-service informational material. Ever the modern entrepreneur, Harry Grief went this ploy one better. He actually hired housewives and little old ladies who, in the normal course of their day spent in supermarkets or sunning themselves, would pass along by word of mouth the tremendous bargains in medical care available at Harry's clinic. Harry was much too bright to pay his word-of-mouth squad in cash. The women he paid in free medical care.

Via synthetic grapevine Harry was able to spread his version of cut-rate, loss-leader, giveaway merchandising to his entire market area which included not only the oldsters still living on the Near North Side but students at the nearby Northwestern University campus, hipsters from the various night spots and clubs, communications men and women from the broadcasting stations, and various artistic types found in the many shops, galleries and ateliers in the neighborhood. Thus Harry managed to rob from the rich and the poor, one of the few doctors of my knowledge who successfully worked both sides of the street.

"All-inclusive physical checkup, $5," was Harry's basic come-on. A rising scale of costs enabled patients to work out their own bills. If printed, the list would go something like this: "With X-ray, $7.50; with blood count, $8.75; with proctoscopy, $10.50 (quite popular among the more epicene of the interior decorator set); with rabbit test, $12.85; with Wassermann, $6.50; with allergy tests, $14.45, etc."

Now, obviously, Harry Grief's range of activities went far beyond that of the typical "blood doctor." Harry realized there was more money to be made with a more diversified service. He had accurately judged his market as containing a high enough quotient of communications-industry types to be shot through with psychosomatic and nervous disorders, tension-produced ailments, hypochondria and the like. Orig-

inally a plain-pipe-racks operation, Harry gradually remodeled his waiting rooms to fit the tastes of his clientele,
installing starkly white walls, black plastic upholstered furni-
ture, and paintings with hot pink impasto.

His prescription-writing technique was and is a model of
modern organization. He has only three basic pills. All are
made up for him by the drugstores in the area. The first is
a mild amphetamine or dexedrine capsule with some caffeine
that gives the patient a slight boost in energy and an emotional lift. The second is a weak barbiturate capsule with a
tranquilizer that calms that patient and soothes anxieties.
The third is a simple APC (aspirin, phenacetin-caffeine) capsule, identical to several trademarked brands, which quells
various minor aches and pains. Harry is thus equipped to handle sluggish and depressed patients, tense and overwrought
patients, and neuralgia types with small-scale twinges of one
kind or another.

The rest he shoos off to an appropriate specialist who kicks
back in cash.

Why should these fairly well-educated patients, few of them
below the national median income, most well above it, believe
in the "all-inclusive" sales approach, the Bauhaus version of
a plain-pipe-racks décor, the carefully bargain-type price, and
the do-it-yourself list of charges? Precisely, it seems to me,
because they have already heard a thing or two about over-
charging and are suspicious to begin with. They normally
comparison-shop. To sum up, perhaps unfairly but accurately, they are inveterate readers of *Consumer Reports*.

Think of it. What a glorious table-turning Harry has accom-
plished. He has led right into his patients' strength and beaten
them. His ploy is analogous to that maneuver in judo wherein
the defender uses an onrushing attacker's momentum to trip
him up and send him sprawling.

Probably the only other doctor I know of to produce much
the same result, but by an entirely different method, was

Arthur Everett Caldecott III, M.D., F.A.C.O.G. He is retired now, but very much a legend in his own time.

The older doctors around Chicago—in their seventies, most of them—refer to him as "Cal." I occasionally run into a woman in her thirties or forties whom Caldecott delivered as a newborn. She is invariably well-to-do.

In a town not as noted for fantastic prices and immense fortunes as, perhaps, New York, Caldecott carved a career for himself—and a permanent niche in the hearts of larcenous doctors everywhere—as the OB-GYN man who charged the highest fees in history.

Surgeons might charge more for an extremely delicate job on an extremely affluent patient. But for sheer gall in demanding $1,000 and even $1,500 to deliver a perfectly normal baby under perfectly normal circumstances—in short, a baby any cabdriver or police sergeant could deliver—Caldecott deserves an equestrian statue in Grant Park.

Happily, Caldecott was a pretty good OB-GYN man. I'd hate to think of some wealthy railroad or pork-packing family paying those kind of prices—in the days when a dollar was a dollar—for a botched job. He also had a series of extremely competent assistants, young men whose functions were only tangentially medical in nature. One of them, who trained with me, once told me over a few beers what life had been like in the halls of the mighty.

Cal Caldecott handled each patient personally. At those prices he could not afford letting a single one out of the range of his powerful personality, his confidence-inducing voice, his crinkly eyes and his firm, warm hands. But there were a lot of details—sometimes called "scut-work"—that a man of Caldecott's stature and reputation simply shouldn't handle. When you were the only OB-GYN man that the wealthy of Chicago would use, you couldn't any longer fool around with blood tests and the like. For that you hired an absolutely crackerjack young specialist, usually fresh out of residency with the very latest techniques firmly in hand, and turned him into what amounted to a lab assistant and male nurse.

My friend described his chief function in this way:

"Cal had a fantastic memory for names," he told me. "He not only knew all the big Chicago families, he knew them down to second cousins twice removed. He knew who'd married who and who'd gotten divorced. If you threw a bride's name at him out of the blue, chances are within a second or two he'd pop right back with the names of her parents, of the groom and his parents and of the siblings on both sides.

"However, Chicago's a pretty big city. Every once in a while a woman would come in whose name didn't ring any bell in Cal's mind. His immense mental reservoirs of genealogy failed to produce a drop of information. And, of course, he was always too much of a gent to ask any point-blank questions. You might ask yourself, well, what the hell, after all, why did Cal need to know this patient's entire family tree? But if you asked that, you just simply didn't understand Cal's operation.

"You see, the only way you could charge $1,500 to deliver a normal baby and not only get away with it, but generate a whole flock of new referrals, gifts at Christmas from grateful patients and all the rest of the trappings of being God to the rich child-bearers of Chicago, is by knowing to the penny how much your patient could afford. That was the reason for Cal's intense interest in genealogy.

"But, as I said, even Cal's fund of information didn't include everyone. So, when a stranger showed up, we had a standard procedure. Cal would give her a very cursory once-over, hardly more than a pulse-and-respiration check, with a blood-pressure reading thrown in for effect. With women of mystery on a first exam, Cal never, absolutely never did an internal or even asked them to so much as remove their gloves.

"But the very next morning he'd be on the phone to them, chuckling at his own absentmindedness. 'I'm terribly sorry, Mrs. Mystery, but in all the rush yesterday I completely forgot to get a blood sample from you. Oh, no, it isn't necessary that you come down here again. I'll send my assistant to your home. No, no trouble. He'll be there in half an hour.' And then, of course, after my decades of highly specialized training, I would hop into action.

"I would show up at the patient's home or apartment and take a few cc's of blood. But in between getting set and doing it and getting unset and what-have-you, I would attend to my real business—casing the joint. I'd check the number of rooms, the décor, the size and appointments, the pictures. Later I'd check the neighborhood and even talk to the doorman or gardener or postman or whomever I could collar.

"In other words, I had spent a lifetime of medical training in order to work as a private eye."

So much for the chief function of Caldecott's assistants. Suffice it to say that on her next visit, the patient was a mystery no longer and Cal could quote his fee with supreme confidence.

My favorite money story isn't about Caldecott, however. It concerns Dr. Emory Falk, of Oak Park, Illinois, a general practitioner for whom I had once done a bit of gynecological surgery in my early years. A few weeks later I happened to be back at the same hospital when Falk hailed me as I got into my car. He came trotting over, all smiles, and stuck his hand in the side window.

"Glad I caught you. I just got paid for that case and I wanted to give you your surgeon's fee."

"Here?" I asked. "Why don't you mail me a check?"

Falk shook his head. "That's not how we do it in Oak Park, Doctor."

He smiled benignly and pulled a fat envelope from his breast pocket. "There," he said, dropping the envelope in my lap so that I could see it was stuffed with ten- and twenty-dollar bills. "Four hundred. Count 'em."

Something about the whole thing didn't seem quite right. Instead of a reputable transaction, the episode was taking on the faint aura of a bookie payoff behind the grandstand. I hefted the envelope and looked at the money.

"I . . . uh, I'm sure it's all here," I said in a tentative way. My inexperienced tone told Falk I hadn't the slightest idea of what to do next.

"That's right, Doctor," he said briskly. "Now, let me show you how we do things in Oak Park." He took back the envelope, counted off two hundred dollars, pocketed the money and returned two hundred to me.

"And that," he said, as he bid me adieu, "is how we do it in Oak Park."

And one or two other places as well.

You Ought to Be Ashamed, Doctor

Not too many patients have told me that. But on the occasions when they have, it has generally been because I have sinned.

There are many more ways for a doctor to sin than for a mere mortal. The Hippocratic Oath alone fixes entire new categories, whole continents and nations of sins which even the lowest of laymen cannot hope to perpetrate. One of the commonest is telling the truth.

For example, Mrs. P.

Mrs. P was an attractive brunette in her mid-forties with an extremely active sex life, as far as I could tell, and four children to prove it. Actually, it was the fourth, age one, who really proved it.

In any event, my sin was not committed with Mrs. P but with her sister Agnes, a younger version of Mrs. P with a lot less on the ball, if you follow me. While I had been Mrs. P's obstetrician for all of her childbearing years, Agnes was a newcomer to me. Her sister brought her along one afternoon, ostensibly to keep her company on a routine visit.

After her own examination, however, Mrs. P wondered if perhaps I might "take a look" at Agnes, Mrs. P had the utmost faith in me; after all, hadn't I delivered all her children and removed that cyst and what not? So perhaps I could just sort of give Agnes a "real thorough checkup."

I did. Agnes was in her thirties and extremely sound, gynecologically speaking. There was absolutely nothing wrong with her, although I did detect some small signs that she had recently undergone a similar examination, perhaps even within the past day or two. It seemed fairly obvious to me that my opinion was the second one the two ladies had solicited. Cautiously, I reexamined her, very thoroughly.

It was then that I committed my first sin. I was no neophyte. I'd been in private practice, at that point, for more than a decade and most of the things that happen in a doctor's office had happened already. I knew that one didn't ask for a second opinion when the patient had been found healthy by the first examiner. Quite the contrary: it's when the first examination turns up something extremely bad that a second opinion is sought.

With that in mind, I nevertheless committed the cardinal sin of telling the bold truth. "Your sister's in perfect health," I told Mrs. P with a big, fat, confidence-inducing smile.

Her face fell, a baffling reaction, to say the least. "Are you sure?" she asked. Agnes, who had gotten her clothes on, now joined us in time to learn the bad news.

"That can't be," she blurted out. "Doctor Smith said it was as big as a tennis ball. Surely you had to notice it."

I leaned back in my chair. It was one of those tumor-as-big-as-the-Ritz cases. "No," I said very firmly, compounding the sin. "No tumor. Not even a cyst. Not even a fibroid. Young lady, you are perfectly fine, healthy and normal."

"You can be frank with us," Mrs. P implored me. "I told Agnes you were absolutely the best. You can tell us the truth. That's why we came to you."

"I'm afraid I have told you the truth. But you don't seem to believe it."

"But, Doctor—"

"Do you feel any tumor?" I asked. "Surely one that big would be impossible to miss."

They stared blankly at me. Such an idea doesn't occur to a really well brainwashed patient. "But, it's inside," Agnes explained feebly.

"Do you feel anything inside?" I persisted.

The two women exchanged glances freighted with arcane meaning. Mrs. P was the first on her feet. "All right," she said in tones usually reserved for humoring the extremely young and feebleminded, "we'll have Dr. Smith check her again. But I don't really expect him to change his finding."

"Neither do I," I said, pounding nails in around the lid of my sin and locking it down for all eternity.

I heard from Mrs. P by telephone two weeks later. "I just had to call," she explained. "I just had to tell you. You ought to be ashamed, Doctor. I've always had such faith in you. I don't know how you could have missed it, but you certainly did. As big as a tennis ball. And he took it out just in time. Another twenty-four hours and he wouldn't have been able to vouch for Agnes's life. I'm certainly glad we decided to go back to him, Doctor, and I thought it only fair that I tell you how close you came to causing a real tragedy. You ought to be ashamed."

Needless to add, I haven't heard from Mrs. P since. She is undoubtedly under the care of the truly miraculous medical man who extracted a tennis-ball tumor out of thin air. I have a feeling he will by now have found several tumors in her, which he has deftly snatched out in the nick of time. He and she are complementary halves of a pair. I suppose, in a sense, they deserve each other.

I shall cut no one whatsoever for the stone.

—from Precepts
attributed to
Hippocrates

Burckhardt

Occasionally a layman—especially one who's seen surgery or has a good imagination—tells you that most surgeons are sadists for whom blood and entrails hold a special psychopathological kick.

The truth is, of course, that surgeons are only doctors who have been trained to cure or alleviate certain illnesses and repair certain defects or injuries by the use of surgery. If surgeons really got their kicks while operating, few could hold a scalpel steady during the fun part. I think it's safe to say that most honest surgeons, offered a course of treatment other than surgery which had the same chance of success, would avoid surgery.

Not so Burckhardt.

He looked quite ordinary. He stood slightly over five feet nine inches in height and he tended toward a certain paunchiness, but not much. He had light brown hair of a healthy thickness and even, dyed color which he kept carefully brushed back from his low forehead. When I first met him, at the very end of the 1930's, he was fully in his prime, no more than fifty-five years old, milky blue eyes unwavering in his rather flat, expressionless face, small button nose giving him a vaguely youthful look, thick neck attesting to substance, solidity, sturdiness and purpose.

As a matter of fact, Burckhardt was a pillar of the medical community. Not only did he regularly attend meetings of the various medical societies, he also led a heavily social life, entertaining his fellow physicians, especially the general practitioners, at all the finest night spots in town. During Prohibition there wasn't a speakeasy of any class where Burckhardt's slightly florid face, shown at the door, wasn't known and welcomed. Burckhardt's professional card, handed through the Judas window of a speakeasy, would gain entry for even a total stranger.

When I met him, in his mid-fifties, Burckhardt was still a bon vivant and general man-about-town, a devotee of the late-closing spots in Harlem, of the old Lindy's just north of Times Square and various clubs along 52nd Street. It was said that he really didn't get going till midnight and he rarely quit until 4 A.M. I have reason to know this was quite true.

At that time it was quite difficult for a medical school graduate to get that valuable last year of internship at a widely known, reputable hospital. Today, internships go begging. In the late 1930's they were a great prize that only a very few could win. A curious characteristic of internships in those days was that the better the hospital, the less money paid the interns. It was my extreme good fortune to be accepted as an intern in a large voluntary hospital in New York with a medical school of renown, where the going pay for interns was a handsome $15 a month.

Our studies were arranged so that in the 12 months of our internship we devoted various amounts of time to each of the hospital's services, from surgery and pediatrics through the emergency room and anesthesia. On my very first day in this exhilarating new environment, filled with pride and excitement and a strong sense of dedication, I drew my first assignment. It read: "Private Surgery; Dr. Burckhardt."

Burckhardt had the use of the hospital's adjoining operating rooms from 4 A.M. every weekday morning until about 7 A.M., at which time the rooms had to be cleaned up and made ready for the hospital's normal daily surgery. He not only had the rooms, he had two scrub (operating room) nurses, two student nurses, two male orderlies, an anesthetist and whatever he required in the way of interns, usually one. In short: Burckhardt and eight staff people.

I arrived that first morning a few minutes before 4 A.M., face shining, eyes bright with anticipation. It didn't matter a hoot to me that interns on other services didn't have to start until 7 A.M., while Burckhardt's boy began three hours earlier. I was full of lofty anticipation.

As I rounded the corner into one of the corridors that led to the operating room I ran head on into a stretcher on which a patient lay waiting. The entire corridor was choked with stretcher carts, patients lying head to toe, jammed together like victims of some terrible highway accident. There were six of them waiting for surgery in this corridor and five in the corridor that led to the second operating room.

"My God," I mumbled to the orderly as I began scrubbing up, "was it some kind of disaster?"

He looked blankly at me. "Huh?"

"All the patients. Explosion? Building collapse?"

He shrugged. "It's an ordinary morning." He mused for a moment. Then: "You should be here on a Monday, Doctor. We sometimes handle twenty of 'em."

Now Burckhardt, scrubbed and gloved and ready to begin, pushed through the swinging doors with his elbows ahead of him. "I'm ready, Doctor," he said in a brisk but kindly tone. His pale blue eyes crinkled in what must have been a smile, although his surgical mask shielded the rest of it. I followed him into the operating room.

What happened for the next three hours at times took on the revved-up look of a Keystone Cops comedy. At other times it reminded me of Charlie Chaplin in *Modern Times*, struggling to keep pace with the assembly line and never quite making it.

"First patient."

Female, Caucasian, 38 years old. Burckhardt's scalpel laid

open her abdomen. Snip. Bit of tissue dropped in a tube. Threaded needle. Stitch-stitch. Uterus suspended to anterior abdominal wall. He turned to me.

"Let me start closing up with the stitch I'd like you to use from now on," he said in a plain, friendly tone. I awkwardly imitated the stitch and as I continued closing up the abdominal wall, Burckhardt disappeared.

The patient was wheeled out. I retired to rescrub. "Ready, Doctor," the scrub nurse called in to me from the other operating room. I ran out under the lights to find Male, Negro, 41 years old, already opened up like a poleaxed steer. Snip. Tissue in tube. Threaded needle. "Here, Doctor," said Burckhardt, "you close him up."

In three hours he opened 12 patients, filed away a few bits of tissue, occasionally did a slight suspension of an organ. So clumsy was I that we didn't finish the last patient until almost 7:10 A.M.

Burckhardt was the soul of solicitude. He watched me panting as I removed my gloves for the last time. My mouth was parched. My eyes were glazed. "Don't worry that we're late," he told me reassuringly.

"We are?"

"That's all right, Doctor. By tomorrow you'll get the swing of it. There's a kind of rhythm to it, you know. It's the Burckhardt rhythm, like a new dance. You'll catch on. But you must never lag behind me that far again," he added in a pleasant, fatherly voice.

I nodded, breathing hoarsely through my mouth. "Right."

He started to say something, but his attention was distracted by the orderly carrying out a tray of labeled tubes containing samples of tissue on their way to Pathology for examination. "Be careful with those," he called. Then, to me: "Some of those growths were pretty far along, wouldn't you say?"

Since I hadn't seen anything like a growth, I merely panted

by way of reply. If I had been asked to recount what little I had seen of Burckhardt's surgery, I would have recalled half-incisions, shallow cuts that removed almost nothing and thin parings of tissue snipped away like cuticle from a fingertip. As far as I could tell—ignorant intern that I was—Burckhardt hadn't done a single piece of real surgery among the entire dozen patients.

"Wouldn't you say?" he asked again.

"Um," I mumbled, luckily still out of breath.

Everything about Burckhardt, of course, was all wrong. The surgery was phony. The need for surgery was non-existent. As the first weeks passed and I began to find my way around, I soon learned that my discovery was rather common knowledge among interns and residents.

When my month with Burckhardt ended, I was happy to leave him. The long corridors choked with patients had begun to get me. The gaping abdomens grinned bloodily at me. I knew enough about procedure to recognize that Burckhardt was a sloppy operator with a cavalier attitude toward the hygienic routine normally practiced in surgery. The parade of tissue snips making their way toward Pathology seemed to be heading toward oblivion. Surely by now someone at the far end of the parade would have cried halt to this callous brutality. The tissue couldn't all be diseased. Whatever the pathologist said about it was not known. Only much later, during my weeks in Pathology, did I learn what happened at the far end of the parade.

Meanwhile, as each new intern did his month with Burckhardt, a sense of outrage began to grow among us. We compared notes. We had satisfied ourselves that there was no reason for his surgery and that all the kindly, twinkle-eyed pleasantness in the world couldn't make up for the monstrousness of what he was doing.

We began to check those records available to us. We learned that the removal of cancerous growths was one of

Burckhardt's more famous specialties, or so his patients' families believed. This kind of operation accounted for more than half the surgery he did. The remainder was for the purpose of breaking up adhesions or doing unnecessary suspensions. Occasionally he was listed as having performed a hysterectomy or the removal of a gall bladder. Curious, I checked back to my first day with him and the first patient of the day, Female, Caucasian, 38 years old. I found she had been officially listed as a hysterectomy, although as far as I could remember the uterus escaped untouched. This was not always the case, however.

Burckhardt's own files were always in a mess. A number of his patients had gone under his knife several times over the years, as you might imagine, and one of my fellow interns scrubbed with Burckhardt the day he opened up a former patient diagnosed as having cancer of the uterus. On finding that her uterus had been removed at some prior date, Burckhardt smoothly snipped off some spare tissue, closed her up again and listed her as another kind of cancer.

Finally, our indignation reached its limit and a handful of us went, as a kind of grievance committee, to the doctor in charge of the intern program. Our complaint was formalized as a refusal to go on duty for Burckhardt at 4 A.M., considering the "nothing" surgery he was performing. For any legitimate reason we would gladly stay up a month of nights. But for Burckhardt, not another hour of lost sleep.

The head of the intern program was a lanky doctor with a slight droop to his left eye, the result of a stroke. He heard us out with not a sign of surprise. Then he smiled very slightly, hardly more than a baring of his teeth.

"You doctors," he began slowly, "you interns will be looking for residencies after this year." It was a statement, not a question. We nodded, anyway.

"You'll look for a residency in a hospital as good as this one. You'll figure that a favorable recommendation from here will carry weight. And it will. You're absolutely right about that." He paused. After a while we realized the pause had gone on too long.

"What about Burckh—"

"So," he interrupted, his bad eye drooping in what seemed to be an evil wink, "anybody that wants a good recommendation certainly won't refuse duty. Because we couldn't possibly recommend anyone who refused duty. I mean, we do have standards to maintain." His bad eyelid lowered even further.

This was, for most of us, our first introduction to real, blue-steel, hard-core corruption, the kind that has protection all the way up and down the line. It was also our first taste of professional fear. True we were always afraid we'd flunk a quiz or an exam. But we were too far along now, with too many years invested in the study of medicine, to take the kind of risk involved in pressing our charges against Burckhardt. We, as the saying goes, "got the message." It was the first of many.

But the fact that we'd been stymied didn't quench our curiosity about Burckhardt. Like a man with a boil who can't keep from touching it, we watched him again and again during the year. How he mobilized 10 to 18 patients a day for surgery eventually became known to us.

He saw nearly 200 patients a week and kept an open surgery schedule. That is, some cases were scheduled weeks in advance for a certain day but, on the day before, if Burckhardt saw he was short 5 or 10 surgery patients for the next morning, he quickly recruited them for the Walpurgis Nacht coming up at 4 A.M.

We learned that the 4-to-7 A.M. group were not Burckhardt's only surgery cases for the day. Tonsils, hemorrhoids and other simple surgery he did right in his office two days a week. You can be sure he knocked off a dozen a day of these about as quickly as a butcher cuts a side of pork into chops.

It came as no deep surprise to learn that Burckhardt also had a large obstetrics practice. Before he checked in at the operating rooms each morning he would make the rounds of those women due for delivery that day. If they hadn't delivered by, say, 4 A.M. or showed no signs of delivering for an hour or two, Burckhardt immediately found reason to reclassify them from a normal delivery to a Caesarean section. Those women not quick enough were then trundled up to wait their turn under the knife for an unnecessary Caesarean which would make it impossible for them ever again to have a normal delivery. Burckhardt made permanent surgery cases out of them.

Like his other surgery, his gynecology and obstetrics were sloppy. Whether it was lack of sleep on his part, or poor training or an overweaning ego or all-consuming greed, Burckhardt was the busiest surgeon in town and probably among the worst.

His patients showed a high complication rate and a higher death rate than the patients of any other surgeon in the hospital. He lost more infants and mothers than anyone else. And yet, as we all knew, he was operating on essentially healthy patients, never removing pathological tissue, cutting out only pieces of organs.

Part of the reason for his high death and complication rates, as I have said, was his lack of technique in either surgery or hygiene. But a great deal of unnecessary illness and death could have been avoided if other doctors, or the residents, had been able to treat his bedridden patients. As it was Burckhardt refused to let anyone touch his patients. He would countermand every order but his own. Although the sulfa drugs were coming into use, and later the antibiotics, Burckhardt refused all of these to his patients. It was literally impossible for anyone, from a nurse to the chief of a service, to have their offer of help accepted. Burckhardt stood alone, refusing even advice. And his patients paid in continued ill-health—or with their lives—for this secrecy.

In this, Burckhardt differed markedly from a charlatan like Hagen, who wouldn't dream of operating on a patient, but insisted on leaving everything to abler hands. Burckhardt's intense need for secrecy was analogous to the bank teller who refuses to take a vacation for fear his defalcations will be discovered when another person checks his books. Burckhardt could ill afford having competent doctors digging about in his patients' affairs. Even the tremendous umbrella of protection he enjoyed could not, ultimately, shield him from too much of that kind of exposure. More to the point, he could not have other doctors even conversing with his patients, for fear that some thin ray of medical reality might penetrate the murk and produce, if nothing else, suspicion of his methods.

At this point, it may be well to ask some embarrassing questions. For example: how good can a hospital be that tolerates a butcher like Burckhardt and provides him with both a cover for his activities and protection when he is found out? Assuming the hospital's training program really was topnotch—and more than mere alumni loyalty compels me to admit it definitely was—what possible reason could the administration have for allowing Burckhardt to continue his contemptible practice?

Answer: no single big reason, but many small compelling ones.

Let's begin with money, always the best place to start when trying to understand corruption. Let's also recall that when I first ran across Burckhardt in the late 1930's he had already been practicing his wholesale butchery for several decades. The country was just beginning to pull up out of the depression and one of the chief reasons the hospital was in fairly decent economic shape at all was Burckhardt's butchery. He and a few other charlatans had kept the hospital from bankruptcy more than once during the depths of the depression. The traffic he created in the operating rooms and laboratories, in wards and private rooms, the medication he prescribed, the anesthesia he called for, the nurses and orderlies he used, all these provided a regular source of revenue for the hospital. Ordinarily, like most voluntary institutions, the hospital relied to some extent on fund-raising campaigns and large donations. This source all but dried up during the depression years. But Burckhardt-inspired revenue continued to flow, a welcome oasis in the economic desert of the 1930's.

With money as our general nexus, let's delve a bit into Burckhardt's socializing. Burckhardt had a great many friends. His politicking in various professional societies was extensive, leading to his being elected chairman of this and secretary of that over a period of years. He was, as I have tried to show, an outwardly friendly, easygoing man with a disarming manner and, I would imagine, a great deal of personal charm in a social situation. At least, many of his colleagues found him charming.

Have I mentioned his egotism? Although he obviously had to know exactly what he was—or rather wasn't—doing, Burckhardt considered himself among the truly great surgeons of the age. In recounting a particular act of savagery, he would objectively describe his work as deft, knowing and far in advance of most of the clumsy oafs who passed for surgeons in those days. A year or two later, when I was a resident at another hospital in New York, it was fascinating, in a macabre way, to end an evening on the town more or less the way Burckhardt did. Sleepy and half looped, we would show up in the theatre seats of the operating room at 4 A.M. to watch Burckhardt cut.

Our presence used to bring out the ham in him to such an extent that we could almost lose sight of what he was doing because his opinion of himself was so ludicrous as to be downright comic. His normal voice was somewhat flat,

with a very slight New England tinge. But when an audience
had gathered for what seemed, to Burckhardt, an educa-
tional purpose, his normal operating-room demeanor would
change, his voice would shift into another tone and tempo
and he would become, almost before our eyes, a corny barker
of the type immortalized by W. C. Fields with a large proportion of the kind of pompous stuffed-shirt exemplified in the
comics by Major Hoople.

"Yeh-as, indeed," he would pontificate. "Mass of adhesions
along the anterior abdominal wall, kaff-kaff. Absolute top-
priority emergency situation. Yeh-as. Here we are. There.
And there. And here. So. Kaff-kaff. Matter's entirely set right,
gentlemen. Entirely." Then, not-so-sotto voce to the luckless
intern assigned him that morning: "Here you are, m'boy.
Ahem. Just, as we might say, sew her up, kaff-kaff, in your
usual fine, nerveless fashion, there's a good fellow. Yeh-as,
indeed. Next customer."

It pains me to admit it, but this kind of blather, accom-
panying as it did some of the worst and most useless surgery
of the century, used to send us into paroxysms of barely sup-
pressed guffaws. With the palm of my hand pressed over my
mouth, I would glance sideways at whatever guests I had
brought to this cruel circus and silently shriek with laughter.
Gone was my sense of outrage. I suppose I did Burckhardt
some small harm by exposing him to half the new doctors in
New York, but I am ashamed to say that his performance
filled us less with horror than with hilarity.

Inevitably, others at the hospital either clashed with
Burckhardt or entered into the conspiracy of silence that
protected him. Several years after I had interned under him,
as I later learned, the old-timer died who had served the
hospital for decades as pathologist. In his place, with a view
toward generally upgrading the staff, a rather brilliant young
pathologist was hired. The previous man had been a partner
of Burckhardt's in many ways: nightly pub-crawling, week-

end golfing and daily lies about the specimens of tissue being removed from Burckhardt's victims. If Burckhardt needed seven verdicts of malignancy that day, for appearances' sake, the pathologist gave him seven. While pathology fraud was nothing new then, or now, the scale on which the old pathologist had practiced it was rather unusual, at least as far as Burckhardt was concerned. I have no idea whether he provided the same favors for any of the other surgeons who practiced at the hospital. To pursue the thought a step further, I have no idea if he could any longer have produced a reliable pathology report even if he wanted to. What is more, I wonder now if anyone in the hospital felt they could rely on his reports or whether all of them were more or less flying blind from time to time, so untrustworthy had his work become.

In any event, one thing I know for certain: the new man was the antithesis of the old. Hardly out of his twenties, he had never had to make the compromises required of a doctor in private practice. He came to the hospital from a highly respected public hospital. I learned from someone inside the hospital that the first time Burckhardt's usual parade of tissue specimens reached him, the new man sent them back with a blanket "No Pathology" report.

It was not like Burckhardt to remonstrate with him. For that day's work, lacking any pathology substantiation, he doctored his records to list a flock of harmless suspensions and the breaking up of adhesions. But you can be certain that he dropped remarks into a number of receptive ears. By late the next day, as the new pathologist was marking the lastest batch of butchery specimens "No Pathology," an informal delegation strolled into his office.

"You see," they finally got around to saying, "it just isn't possible for Dr. Burckhardt to be so consistently wrong, now is it?"

"Right," the new man readily agreed. "As a matter of fact,

if I catch him pulling this kind of stuff tomorrow, the third day in a row, I'm going to bring him up on charges."

"No, no, you miss our point," he was told. "We believe if you restudy your findings, you'll see that there had to have been some pathology present."

The new man eyed the delegation with distaste. "No mistake. No pathology."

After a bit more fencing, the delegation put it on the line: "It makes the hospital look bad when one of its busiest surgeons isn't backed up by Pathology."

"Not as bad," the new man remarked between gritted teeth, "as fake pathology reports would. Surgeons can make mistakes. Pathologists can't. Do you want to give out the idea you've got a pathology department that doesn't know what it's doing?"

"N-no," the delegation assured him in tones that indicated the answer was really yes. "Well, then, look here: suppose you just don't file any reports on Burckhardt's specimens. That way everybody's happy."

After a great deal of back-and-forth, this was actually the plan of action—or rather non-action—followed by the pathologist for the next few weeks. He was young and anxious to please, but his early years in public service had spoiled him with a heady whiff of what honest medicine could be like. The uneasy compromise was doomed. It was only a matter of a month before the new pathologist returned to the bosom of the public hospital where he'd been underpaid, overworked but fairly honest.

You would want to know, I expect, that the pathologist who replaced him was also a youngster, fresh out of residency, whose name was Burkhart. This was no coincidence. He was a first cousin of Burckhardt's, once removed, whose family had simplified the spelling of the name.

It would be pointless now to try to psychoanalyze Burckhardt by remote control, so to speak. The man has been dead for several years. My own close contact with him was of only a month's duration. In the entire city you would not find a doctor who had ever worked closely with Burckhardt for more than a month. His associates, allies, protectors, fellow conspirators and cousins would hardly be impartial observers of the man. To this day, I would imagine, most of them have only the fondest of memories about their benefactor and friend.

Perhaps some of his chronic patients might provide a starting place for recreating the man's personality. Research might begin with a few of the poor Irish families from the West Side or the Upper East Side who seemed almost pre-ordained to serve as Burckhardt's meat, in the literal sense. There were families of seven and eight, all of whom could boast at least one abdominal scar courtesy of Burckhardt. Some could produce two or more.

Hatcheck girls in nightclubs could probably give you some insights into Burckhardt. His anesthetists and scrub nurses might, except that they would be afraid of implicating themselves as accessories. Why talk now? Why not have talked decades ago and saved dozens, perhaps hundreds, of lives? No help there.

Perhaps it's not possible anymore to know exactly what made Burckhardt tick. He may have enjoyed the night life, the dissipation, and turned to operating room crime to finance his pleasures. We knew he played the horses. We knew women played him. He had a rather imposing mansion on Upper Fifth Avenue, some 400 acres in New Hampshire with hunting lodge and private lake, and beach retreats on both Long Island Sound and the Caribbean. He had to split some of his fees and we knew he couldn't hit many of his patients for much more than a few hundred per operation. Obviously only sheer volume could finance such a life style.

But this is a simplistic view of the man: he needed money, so he committed crimes. Considering the vast size of the estate he left behind him, it seems obvious that Burckhardt was clearing a great deal more than he needed to feed his appetite for high living. Was it, after all, only the American Dream, Surgeon Style? Did he really do anything more than a latter-day Vanderbilt or Mellon or Jay Gould? Wasn't he simply a Robber Baron in White?

This, too, doesn't fully explain Burckhardt. The economics of the situation go a fair way toward explaining the sheer numbers of people he cheated and killed. But the rest is darkness. What can explain the forced Caesareans? Is there any greed so immense that it can be a reason for the poor hygiene? Did proper scrub-up and hygienic procedure cost Burckhardt anything extra? Or, by slowing him down a minute or two on each operation, would proper hygiene have proved that costly to him? Can one conceive of avarice alone creating the illusion in Burckhardt's mind that he was, in fact, a truly great surgeon? Or, were his wild fantasies about his own proficiency merely cover stories, big lies designed to distract attention from what he was doing?

If you want to think about Burckhardt, either as a unique individual or perhaps as a type, even as a prototype, of the kind of man who succeeds so gloriously in our society, then you must know a few more things about him.

You must know, for example, about Helen J.

Helen J. was a small twelve-year-old whose parents and elder brothers were all patients of Burckhardt. As a matter of fact, Burckhardt had delivered Helen. Now, having begun to menstruate somewhat earlier than normal, Helen was having a few problems. The onset of each period was painful and, on one occasion, the cramps grew so severe that Burckhardt smelled big money. He decided she had appendicitis. He cut Helen J. open at 5:15 A.M. on a Monday, one of 14 operations he performed that morning. Helen was wheeled into a private room and remained under sedation.

She began to develop a fever. The floor nurse called

Burckhardt at midnight, locating him at Jimmy Ryan's, on 52nd Street. When he learned that Helen was running a temperature of 104, Burckhardt promised the floor nurse he'd be over within a few minutes. In point of fact, however, he arrived at the hospital at his usual 4 A.M., operated on 17 patients and was on the point of leaving for his office when a message the floor nurse had left caught up with him and reminded him about Helen.

The prolonged fever had produced a somewhat comatose state. Helen failed to respond to questions. The resident suggested the presence of peritonitis.

"Not at all," Burckhardt was heard to state. "You take out an appendix that inflamed and you're bound to have a sharp reaction. Ten grains of aspirin every three hours. Plenty of fluids." He left the hospital.

On Wednesday night, at about 11 o'clock, Burckhardt received a call at an East Side club. Helen J. was dead. Burckhardt rushed to the hospital to get there before Helen's parents did. He was able to meet them in the public lobby as they arrived. Solicitously, he ushered them through the darkened corridors to the room where, shades drawn, a murky half light showed them the bluish-white face of their dead daughter.

Burckhardt was all compassion. He bought them coffee in the cafeteria. He told them a long story about how extensive the pathology had been, how much of a head start the infection had had, what a brave girl Helen had been during the long hours he'd sat by her bed. The words flowed on. Then he left them, tranquilized under this thunderous barrage of clichés and the terrible access of their grief.

Unfortunately for Burckhardt, one of those maddening coincidences then occurred. Before Helen J.'s parents had been able to gather themselves together and leave the cafeteria, the resident physician who had suggested peritonitis arrived for coffee. From having visited Helen in her room a few hours after the operation, her mother recognized the resident. On their way out of the cafeteria, the parents nodded.

"Thank you," the mother said, "for what you did for Helen."

I don't suppose anything else she might have said would have produced the result this did. She could have cut him dead, kicked him in the shins or fainted away on the cafeteria floor without inducing the resident to talk.

He took the parents by the arm to a quiet corner of the cafeteria. "I did nothing for Helen," he said then. "I believe you ought to sign a permit for an autopsy."

The parents recoiled, a common reaction to the thought of permitting a loved one's body to be further desecrated. But the resident persisted, calmly and with great logic.

His motives, by the way, were blameless. True, he wanted to justify his own suspicion of peritonitis. True, he wanted very much to unmask Burckhardt as a fraud and a murderer. But, actually, it was his duty as the resident to try to get an autopsy permit signed. Reputable hospitals require a certain number of autopsies. If there were time enough, they would urge an autopsy in every death. But they especially require an autopsy after a death that, in Helen's case, was somewhat puzzling.

"It won't help the poor girl now," the father demurred.

"But it'll help us. Maybe we'll learn something that can help the next person," the resident urged.

"Learn what? You mean it wasn't appendicitis? There's some doubt?"

"That's what autopsies are for," the resident persisted, unwilling to commit himself to more than that.

The parents conferred for a moment. "We want to ask Dr. Burckhardt about it first. We have a lot of faith in him. Dr. Burckhardt delivered all our kids and took care of my wife's gall bladder and we sort of depend on him."

The resident's mouth stayed shut. He nodded once and left.

The telephone conversation with Burckhardt was short and not sweet. Fortunately the hospital operator neglected to tell Helen's parents where she located the doctor in whom they had such faith. He had moved on from the East Side club to an apartment in the high 60's where a single lady of his acquaintance made her home. It was now about 2 A.M.

"Absolutely not!" Burckhardt exploded. "When you want to know something, you talk to me, not to some flunky! Why on earth should you let them experiment with that poor girl's body? Don't sign anything, you hear me? Don't sign anything!"

Although his lady friend did her best to soothe Burckhardt and although Helen's parents had promised not to sign an autopsy permit, Burckhardt found it difficult to relax after this disturbing telephone call. It was always possible the parents might change their minds. Between now and tomorrow morning someone could convince them to sign a permit. There was always a resident pathologist on duty, eager enough for practice. Burckhardt could well find out, by morning, that he was in a great deal of trouble.

Just before 3 A.M., the night man at a funeral home near the hospital saw a Cadillac pull up to the side entrance. Since he recognized his caller as Burckhardt, he didn't think anything strange about the fact that the bundle Burckhardt carried inside and laid on the zinc contained the thin body of a twelve-year-old girl. She had been wrapped first in oilcloth bearing the hospital's name and then in a dirty blanket of the kind occasionally found in the trunks of cars. By morning, Helen J. was embalmed and ready for burial.

Burckhardt reported to surgery at his usual 4 A.M. and performed 12 operations before 7 A.M. Long before that time the corpse was reported missing from the hospital's morgue. Burckhardt went home at about 7:30 A.M. and slept for a while. He was roused by a frantic phone call from the hospital at 9:30 A.M. Did Burckhardt have any idea at all where the body might be?

He told them.

Burckhardt brazened out the storm that followed, never once straying from his firm conviction that, in their grief, the parents didn't remember that they had definitely asked him to arrange for the girl's funeral preparations. As to why it had been done so hurriedly in the hours after midnight, Burckhardt's explanation was reasonable enough. He'd put in a long, hard day. It wasn't until after midnight that he'd found time to expedite matters. Why personally? Why not? He'd been fond of Helen. Hadn't he brought her into the world? He wanted to be sure they did a really first-rate embalming job on her. Why take her out of the hospital alone and unnoticed? Sheer coincidence his not being seen. He'd certainly made no attempt to avoid meeting anyone. Perhaps they hadn't been on duty, where they should have been. Perhaps questions should be asked as to where they'd actually been when they were supposed to be at the morgue. Perhaps. . . .

The technique is an old and good one. Scatter suspicion freely. Stir up guilts with a broad spoon. But never change your own story by a word.

The parents' tale of talking to the resident was confirmed. But when it came to determining who said what, the resident grew vague, cut what losses he could and helped rescue Burckhardt with his own silence.

Let me speculate. It might have happened this way. It's dark. The morgue is temporarily deserted. The seven-foot-long refrigerated drawers are hard to see by the tiny light over the desk near the door. Without making a sound, the door swings slowly open.

A man edges silently inside the room. He moves along the row of drawer handles, squinting in the darkness. Finally he drops to one knee and I hear his cigarette lighter. By its tiny flame he reads the tag on a drawer, then pulls it open.

The hospital sheet is clammy with cold. He draws back one edge for a moment and stares at the girl's face. His own is immobile. Even the flickering flame of the cigarette lighter doesn't give his face a single spark of animation. He covers her face again.

She's terribly light, less than 80 pounds. But when he lifts her his face contorts with the effort; he must be careful not to bend her midriff. The stitches may not hold and her entrails may cascade out onto the corridor floor.

There are only two more bad parts: carrying her body into the car he has parked in the alley and carrying her body out of the car into the funeral home.

And Burckhardt, who brought her into the world, ushers her out.

Burckhardt died at the age of seventy, leaving an estate of between $2 and $3 million. Several of his children were named as heirs. They are still fighting over the money.

The Discount Doctor

It is now my distinct pleasure to tell you about a nice guy, Dahlman the Discount Doctor, the man who single-handedly carried medicine forward into the plain-pipe-racks, half-off-list-price era.

We used to refer to Dahlman as the living doll. If a need ever arose—supply your own situation—for you to request the shirt from his back, Dahlman would whip it off in an instant . . . gladly. Dozens of doctors around New York, myself included, were beholden to Dahlman for so many things that they could never repay the debt, even if Dahlman considered it a debt which, of course, he didn't.

I met him under extremely harrowing circumstances one night when I was still in my first year as a resident at a large voluntary hospital in Manhattan. The events which led up to the meeting are another story. Suffice it to say that in coping with a problem delivery, the attending doctor and I had gotten into a bad situation and time was running out. The other doctor called Dahlman, whose office was directly across the street from the hospital on the ground floor of a building in which he also lived. Dahlman arrived within five minutes, surveyed the wreckage of our bungling and in a few moments of absolutely inspired manipulation, delivered the baby and saved the day.

We retired to the doctors' lounge for coffee and I offered Dahlman some of the hospital's Danish pastry. He gave me a stricken look, got on the phone and within a few minutes a delivery boy had arrived from a nearby delicatessen with a dozen assorted sandwiches, cartons of cole slaw and potato salad and bottles of beer. That was Dahlman. He not only refused any payment for the delivery, he lavished food on the residents who, at that time, were earning about $25 a month, plus room and board. Dahlman knew that the "board" furnished by the hospital, for both staff and patients, was probably the worst food east of the Mississippi River, if not the Continental Divide.

Food was important to Dahlman. He was a big man with large, awkward-looking hands and eyes like a basset hound. I have heard him referred to as a gangling hulk, a good-natured dope and one of the best obstetricians in New York City. I can attest to the latter. Having been trained as a gynecologist, what proficiency I have as an obstetrician I owe to the privilege of working with Dahlman. He may not have understood the latest theoretical information, but as a technician he had few equals.

In addition to his work and good food, Dahlman had few other interests. He was not someone with whom you could discuss the Nazi invasion of Poland, the defeat of Wendell Willkie or any of the other events that stirred people in those years, such as Betty Grable's legs and the way Walters shut out the Tigers in the sixth game of the World Series. His mind, we all agreed, was somewhat slow-moving. But, while none of us gave him high marks for brightness, we considered him a real natural, a gifted practitioner who shed his shambling exterior and air of dullness when he delivered a baby.

Dahlman was like some giant animal of the sea, graceful in his element, awkward out of it. More than that, he didn't have much practical sense, especially about money. His fees were low to begin with and—whether out of altruism or poor judgment—he was known throughout the five boroughs of New York City for offering discounts.

This was an era in which the discount as we know it today didn't exist. You got 2 percent off for paying cash in ten days, but the whole concept of a list price which was discounted in order to attract customers simply was unknown to retailers and their customers.

Into this Garden of Eden situation, Dahlman introduced the modern concept of a discount. It worked this way. His normal fee for prenatal care, delivery and a six-week checkup afterward was $150. Many obstetricians charged $200 or even $300 to the same class of patient Dahlman served. They sneered at his low fees and called them obvious evidence of poor judgment. "An obstetrician, yes. A businessman, hah!"

But Dahlman wasn't content with a "list" price lower than some of his contemporaries. He also let it be known that to certain women with certain characteristics he would allow a discount off list. $125, not $150!

Who were these fortunate women? Any clergyman's wife qualified. So did the wife of any teacher in the public schools.

The wives of policemen, firemen, civil service workers, serv-
icemen, employees of Consolidated Edison, the Bell System,
any bank or savings and loan association, the A & P, any
department store, the subways, bus lines and El, dock workers, cab drivers, members of Musicians Union Local 802, the
ILGWU, the Furriers' union and anyone who was expecting
Baby Number Two or more—all these were eligible for Dahlman's discount.

To this small, select group Dahlman admitted anyone else
who asked for the discount or even vaguely referred to it in
passing.

You will not be surprised, therefore, to learn that he delivered an average of 600 babies a year, nearly two a day, if you
don't include Sundays.

In addition, of course, he did a certain amount of gynecological work, handled "women's" problems and the like and
was available in emergencies, as we have seen, at the voluntary hospital across the street from his office. He visited us at
least once a day to pass the time for a half hour or so. Usually
he brought food, candy, bakery goods or cigarettes. Occasionally he arrived with a box of cigars. In anyone else, so conditioned have we become to the what's-in-it-for-me? syndrome,
we would have been extremely wary of such generosity. It was
obvious that Dahlman wanted nothing from us and, indeed,
with a practice like his, needed nothing we could give him.

One thing all of us itched to give him was advice, to take
Dahlman in hand and teach him the economic facts of life.
Attending doctors at the hospital, hard-bitten veterans of the
doctoring racket, used to shake their heads in pity.

"He's no kid," they'd say. "He's in his fifties. What will he
live on when he gets too old to handle that kind of volume?
How will he get along when he can't work at all? The smart
thing would be to charge a good fee now, while he's still
active, and salt away a buck or two for his old age."

A few of the young residents at the hospital became special

favorites of Dahlman. I was one of those he would invite across the street to dinner once or twice a week. His wife had been a nurse in the obstetrics department of the hospital and still helped her husband at the office. She was also an excellent cook, as any wife of Dahlman's would of necessity have to be. The dinners were always delicious, bountiful but not fancy: shrimp, a good steak, salad and some terribly rich dessert. The two or three of us lucky enough to get an invitation would loll back in our chairs after dinner, riveted to the seat beneath us, eyes glazed with good living, not a thought in our heads of the cot we slept in across the street or the whole, entire $25 we could squander during the next month. Thanks to Dahlman and his wife we had escaped from reality for a few wonderful hours.

At Christmas there were always presents for us. We might bring the Dahlmans some small token of our thanks, but for us they had gifts of real substance: small radios, electric shavers, pieces of luggage, 8-day traveling clocks.

By now you have a pretty clear picture of this man. Not terribly intelligent, but all heart. No understanding when it came to practical matters, but all-enveloping in his human feelings and generosity. He literally had no life except his practice and his generosity toward young residents. When you handle 600 deliveries a year you have precious little time to do much more than that.

As it must to all men, the end of my residency came to me. I was chucked headlong into private practice and for the first few months I literally had no idea where my first dollar was coming from. It was during this time that I realized how great a friend Dahlman really was. Although he was on call 24 hours a day to his patients, he occasionally couldn't find the time or energy in the middle of the night to answer an emergency call. Instead he would assure the patient that an unusually competent doctor would attend her, wake me up and send me on my way.

You may think it less than pleasant to be awakened at 3
A.M. of a cold, rainy night to travel a dozen miles because
someone may or may not be hemorrhaging. The fee was sometimes as much as $20, in cash, collected from the patient after
the call. And Dahlman was very strict about it: what I col-
lected I kept. Before I went to bed, therefore, I usually sent
up a fervent prayer that one of his $20 calls would wreck my
sleep that night.

In this way, I was fortunate enough to keep sporadically
busy during those first days of private practice. Others who
had gone out into the world with me weren't as lucky. And
because he was the kind of man he was, Dahlman would occasionally tell one of his patients, whose problems were gynecological and not obstetrical, that she should transfer to me on
a permanent basis. Thus it was that I found myself after a
while with a handful of patients, long before many of my colleagues had located their first, all thanks to Dahlman.

Suddenly, with no warning at all, he had a heart attack.

I say "no warning." It should have been obvious, even to
an obstetrician, that his workload would have felled an ox,
but Dahlman had never once slackened his pace, not in 20
years or more. Now he was forced to stop work entirely.

His wife and I and a few of his medical friends held a conference beside his bed. It was decided that I would take over
the bulk of his practice now, with some assistance from others
and that, when Dahlman was able to work again, I would
remain with him for about six months, gradually transferring
the workload back on his shoulders. It was also agreed that by
the time he was able to carry a full load he would have cut
down on the size of his practice by at least a half, that he
would deliver 300 babies a year or even fewer and that the
remainder of his patients would just have to find themselves
another doctor.

That he'd gone this long without a heart attack should
have prepared us for the fact that Dahlman did, indeed, have

the constitution of an ox. Within a month he was back at the office a few hours a day, supervising me and another man who came in once a week.

It was then I learned how Discount Doctoring worked.

You must understand that Dahlman was basically honest, or as honest as the next man, or perhaps more honest than that, but not much. For instance, the $125 discount fee was a legitimate proposition. If the prospective mother had no complications, complained of no problems and went through an uneventful delivery the price was $125, right enough.

But let her once, at any time during the nine months, even casually mention a pain in the small of her back, a stain in her underpants or a faint queasiness in the stomach and Dahlman had her in the palm of his hand. Everything became an extra. The $125 fee included prenatal visits, if I remember correctly. But the moment you complained of something you needed extra treatments and they cost you a modest enough fee . . . extra.

You probably needed shots, too. You needed return visits and more shots. Other doctors might charge $10 or even $15 a shot. Dahlman charged $3.71, "exactly" what it cost him. It cost, in fact, about 75 cents, but even so his price was lower than those of other doctors.

The hard-bitten veterans of obstetrics who laughed at Dahlman and pitied his lack of business acumen had no idea that by labeling routine treatment as extraordinary, Dahlman was collecting $200 and more for a perfectly normal pregnancy (known to his patients as a "problem pregnancy").

And all of it was paid in cash, on the spot, at the time of treatment. Mrs. Dahlman wore a special uniform she had designed. On the right side it sported a large patch pocket with an opaque lining. By the end of a typical day this pocket would be bulging with fives and tens.

But Discount Doctoring didn't end with the delivery of the child. It extended to the visit six weeks after birth when many of the mothers inquired about a diaphragm. For some it was their first; others simply assumed they'd need one in a different size, following the birth.

Dahlman didn't charge for measuring and fitting a diaphragm. Here, too, his colleagues pitied his poor sense of business. None of them charged less than $15 for this service, which included the diaphragm free of added charge, since it rarely cost them more than a dollar.

Dahlman did it differently. Since each of the ladies he measured presented a special problem, each required a special diaphragm. Let me explain that diaphragms come in a few sizes, one of which will fit virtually anybody more or less snugly. The more or less is part of the breaks of the game. After all, both the woman and the diaphragm are flexible and elastic and, anyway, who ever said a diaphragm was 100 percent effective?

But the standard sizes didn't fit these ladies. They had to come back a week later—at $10 a visit—and because it was a special order the diaphragm cost $10. So Dahlman the poor businessman ended up collecting $20 for what his colleagues charged $15.

At the end of six months I had delivered 273 babies and was about to become a thirty-one-year-old cardiac case. Without a single regret I turned his practice back to Dahlman with my blessing. I estimated that in a normal month he took in more than $16,000, or an average of nearly $200,000 a year.

Poor, not-very-bright Dahlman, King of Discount Doctoring. He's retired now and living where the sun only stops shining at night. A lot of doctors wonder how in hell he managed to scrape together a few miserable dollars for his retirement. They just don't understand Discount Doctoring, or Dahlman, either.

... that I will exercise my art solely for the cure of my patients and will give no drug, perform no operation, for a criminal purpose, even if solicited, far less suggest it. ...

—from the Oath of
Hippocrates

The Economics of Abortion

I would assume that deliberate abortions are probably as old as the human race. There are even examples of monkeys aborting themselves, but only a monkey could be certain it was deliberate.

While some fairly knowledgeable people believe that abortion is a highly controversial subject—especially for doctors to discuss—the facts are otherwise. There are almost no controversies concerning abortion. It is practiced almost universally, in both primitive and sophisticated communities, has been for many centuries and continues to be as you read these words.

Abortion is as common as fornication. The two acts share one characteristic in addition to their more obvious cause-and-effect relationship. Both are practiced at every level of society. But while fornication is often called the great leveler, abortion is the great differentiator.

In this era of pop fashion, ready-made clothing and universal education, it may occasionally be difficult to tell a poor girl from a rich one at first, careless glance. But in the kind of abortion they can afford, you will find a brutally accurate indicator of their caste, class and income.

For most women, under the proper conditions, an abortion is simple and quick. If this is true, and I assure you it is, then why do women die of abortion or require a hysterectomy while still in their twenties? The answer is money.

The well-to-do can get an abortion easily, safely and

175

"legally." The lower middle class of wage earners, their wives and girl friends, secretaries and office workers—these people, too, can get a safe abortion although it will not be as easy to get or as "legally" performed.

But the poor will pay with their lives and their future happiness. The poor will pay with the only coins they have: pain, blood and death.

Let's visit what the resident doctors refer to, not very secretly, as the "abortion ward" of a large public hospital in Chicago. Obviously the ward is not meant to be set aside for the performing of abortions, although many are completed here. The purpose of the ward is to treat impoverished women who are sick, at times near death, as the result of the only kind of abortions they can afford.

I will not sicken you with a list of the types of things introduced into the uterus by would-be abortionists to induce premature labor and rid the woman of her embryo. Among the most common are catheters or drains of one kind or another, chemical douches, prods and sticks of various types.

These brutal manipulations are performed under conditions of dirt and squalor. No attempt is made to keep the operator or the patient clean, let alone antiseptic. Hands are dirty. Tools are dirty. Beds or floors or chairs on which the woman lies are dirty. The operator has only a rudimentary idea of female anatomy. The patient is too ignorant to realize the danger she faces.

If she is lucky, she may find an abortionist who is or has been a nurse, midwife, hospital orderly or aide. Such a person may have a few glimmerings of hygiene and anatomy. Their fee is much higher. More often, however, the impoverished pregnant victim puts herself in the hands of someone totally without background, who makes a few dollars of blood-money from her fear and shame.

What can women like this pay? They are taken literally for every cent they can raise, but whether they pay $5 or $50, what they are buying is an invitation to death. The abortion wards of the public hospitals are filled with one tragedy after another, teen-age girls who will never bear children again, married women who die of infection.

At the upper edge of the poorest classes, where the income level begins to shade into the lower middle class, we find another kind of abortionist who mulcts the poor on either side of the borderline. He is usually a G.P. and his chief stock in trade is some abortifacient, a pill or injection which is supposed to "bring around" the woman long past her period and obviously pregnant. No such abortifacient exists. If it did, and it were an inexpensive pill of some kind, perhaps this would not need to be written. But, although there is treatment that can bring on a temporarily delayed menstrual flow, none can produce a period once a woman is pregnant.

In order to stay well on the right side of the law, the nostrum abortionist plays it smart as to what he does and doesn't promise.

> PATIENT: ... so if there's anything you could do, Doctor, I'd ... I'd ...
>
> DOCTOR: There is one thing. It may help, although there are cases where the embryo is just so firmly fastened that, well, nothing helps. But—
>
> PATIENT: (*hysterical joy*) I'll try it! Right away!
>
> DOCTOR: That's three injections at ten dollars each.

It doesn't really matter what is in the hypodermic syringe. It can be a drug like prostigmine to stimulate bleeding. It can be a plain saline solution. In either event, if within a few weeks the woman's period ensues, she is overjoyed and delirious with gratitude. The doctor has saved her. You can be sure she will tell all her friends. If the injections fail, the doctor shakes his head and shrugs. He'd warned her, hadn't he?

Since many a woman who fancies herself pregnant is merely

a few weeks late, the injection-type abortionist usually has a loyal, grateful and extremely extensive following.

Those who sing his praises include women of the lower middle class, but it is more likely that when one of them is actually pregnant—especially if the injection abortionist has failed her—she will turn to another doctor who does actual abortions.

Who are these doctors? Some are already outside the law, have been caught before, may even have done time. They can no longer practice legitimate medicine. Their only income is from abortions. Others are still personae gratae, still hold their license, may still have hospital affiliations of one sort or another. They do occasional abortions, usually in their offices. Still others are hidden away in certain towns or states. The "scene" shifts from year to year. One year it's New Jersey where all the Easterners go. Puerto Rico has a similar reputation. So do towns in Pennsylvania and Florida, from time to time. Pre-Castro Cuba was a very popular abortion center. Certain other Latin-American locales achieve underground prominence on occasion.

Whether the professional abortionist performs the operation in his office, some secluded private clinic, the patient's home or a rented room in a no-questions-asked transients' hotel, what he basically does is to dilate the cervix, insert a curette, or scraping tool, and scrape the walls of the uterus free of tissue. This is removed and discarded. The operation under these illegal circumstances is most often performed without anesthesia because the patient must be ready to walk out of the doctor's life immediately. It is a painful experience although, if done properly, not a very risky one. The jargon term for it is known to most women as cleaning or a D-and-C —dilation and curettage—and the operation itself has other, more legal, uses. It is legitimately employed to clear out infection or possible sources of infection after a miscarriage, as a diagnostic aid and as a treatment for various conditions, including polyps.

For the typical single or married secretary or office worker, the unmarried girl whose boyfriend can't or won't marry her, or the married woman who doesn't want any more children, this illegal abortion costs between $200 and $500. This is not an exorbitant fee if the operation is skillfully performed under properly hygienic conditions. Nevertheless, these patients are well advised to see their own doctor afterwards and head off any complications caused by careless work.

For about the same fee or a bit more, the woman who has a regular family G.P. can obtain a somewhat classier abortion. It is only slightly illegal and usually includes a bit of well-earned bed rest as a reward.

The kindly old family G.P., once he's reluctantly agreed to do this thing, inserts some kind of probe into the uterus under hygienic conditions. He may even use a common Q-tip swab. He agitates this probe for a few minutes, hoping to set up a local reaction within the uterus that will result in a miscarriage. If he is skillful and lucky he may in a few cases be able to induce such a reaction, in which case the patient goes into labor, aborts, passes all the product of the process and in due time is as good as new. This, of course, is the exception, rather than the rule.

More often, by fiddling about as he has, the G.P. causes infection. He may produce a certain amount of bleeding. In either event he has created the opportunity to pass his patient along to a gynecologist with a request for a D-and-C to clear out the infection or the presumed miscarriage.

Once the gynecologist takes over—whether he suspects the truth or not and, if he does, he overlooks it for a fee—he can sign the patient into the cleanest, prettiest, best hospital in town, curette her at both their leisures and reward her with a few days of rest and sleep in bed. In effect, the gynecologist has performed an abortion, but all quite legally, since it was the G.P. who induced it. No one makes a practice of wondering aloud why the G.P. found an infection or bleeding.

Obviously we have now reached another border on the money road. We are in the area between the middle class and the wealthy. The G.P.-to-specialist abortion is almost the best money can buy. It can't get anyone in trouble. The G.P. doesn't run the risk of bungling the job by perforating the uterus or pulling down an intestine or some other botched giveaway. The specialist is covered by the G.P.'s diagnosis. And the patient gets first-class hospital treatment all the way.

The only thing better than this costs quite a bit more, somewhere between $750 and $2,000. But it's worth every cent. It's the perfectly legal, virtually risk-free abortion, performed in broad daylight in the best hospital in town. Only the rich settle for nothing less and only the rich can afford it.

> DOCTOR: Yes your guess was right. You're pregnant.
>
> PATIENT: How dull. I simply can't be, Doctor.
>
> DOCTOR: *(In his most ethical tones)* I'm afraid you are and there's very little we can do about it.
>
> PATIENT: I'm sure you can think of something.
>
> DOCTOR: *(Thinking of the fees he's charged this woman, her friends and her relatives, all of whom come to him on her recommendation)* Well, of course, we know there's something we can do. It's just that I'd hate to have it done by anybody else but me. And I don't do too much of that work, you know.
>
> PATIENT: But you can make an exception in my case, can't you?
>
> DOCTOR: It's terribly expensive. A lot of people have to get paid and, of course, I wouldn't want to do it except in the best possible hospital we can get. *(Here he mentions a few of the most expensive, prestigious hospitals in town.)*
>
> PATIENT: *(Relieved and smiling)* Shall we say this Friday?

Now the doctor has two choices: he can simply check her into the hospital, perform a D-and-C and put down any murmurs from the resident doctors with a show of standing, seniority and professional superiority. Or he can rehearse with his patient a very simple medical history she can give the resident when he makes his rounds: bleeding, pain, tissue passed, etc., all the symptoms of a miscarriage for which, of course, she now requires a D-and-C. Either way the abortion is performed without recourse to Q-tip diddling, risk of infection and the like.

Every big voluntary hospital in the country is the scene of these abortions, week in, week out. How do doctors get away with it? The fact is they're rarely challenged. They call the D-and-C necessary because the patient has either had a miscarriage, an incomplete miscarriage or a threatened "inevitable" miscarriage. They're known as reputable OB-GYN men. They have the run of the operating room. How can they possibly be questioned?

And, if they are, does anything serious befall them? I recall one instance in which a particular gynecologist had been doing at least an abortion a week at a steady clip. Finally one of the residents could stand it no longer. Something in his personal code of ethics made him rebel, whether out of conscience or religious conviction or what, I never found out. In any event, he blew the whistle, made the charge and supplied enough background to make it stick. The gynecologist in question still practices at the hospital. But where he once performed a D-and-C a week, he may do only three a year. The hospital keeps a very sharp eye on him. Why, the poor fellow is forced to do most of his abortions elsewhere.

If this de-luxe-type abortion, with all its trimmings and its free-and-easy air of camaraderie, is so eminently possible in any big city—and virtually every major voluntary hospital in the country has been playing host to such abortions for years —why can't middle-class working girls take out a personal loan for a few thousand dollars and get the same treatment?

The answer lies partly in the question of security for the doctor. It is true, of course, that both patient and abortionist are guilty in the eyes of the law. In that sense one cannot inform on the other without implicating himself, unless he has made an immunity deal with the district attorney. But life is more complex than that when one is in the upper income brackets, as some doctors and some of their patients are.

What if a well-heeled doctor who occasionally does abortions agreed to accept $2,000 from a mere nobody? Does that mere nobody have as much to lose in reputation and income if the abortion is discovered? Obviously the jeopardy must be of the same order on both sides of the deal, or the deal cannot be consummated.

In addition to protecting himself, the occasional abortionist must also protect his future sources of legitimate income. The woman who asks him for an abortion, as I have noted, may be responsible for referring him tens of thousands of dollars of legitimate business. To turn her down would be to risk losing the custom of her friends and relatives.

There are other pressures to which the "legal" abortionist often yields. If another doctor asks him to perform an abortion on a sister, wife or mistress, can the abortionist refuse? As a legitimate OB-GYN man, he depends as much on referrals from other doctors as he does from well-fixed patients.

There are inner pressures as well, the need for money being the primary and overriding one. But why should a gynecologist with a $50,000-a-year practice in legitimate treatment stoop to perform an abortion for a few paltry thousand? Cash.

In a society increasingly audited by Big Brother Government, where computers are capable of matching a doctor's tax return against the records of those who paid him money in that year, unrecorded cash has become a commodity with far more than its face value.

Individual doctors have more individual needs for cash. One man here in Chicago has a very lucrative private practice, is married to a railroad heiress, has an apartment in Marina City and an estate in Evanston. Between them, he and his wife must enjoy a net worth well up in the several millions. Yet, I know he does at least one abortion a month for about $2,000. This creates for him a cash income of about $24,000 a year. It's more than enough to pay the rent for the small flat on Ohio Street in Old Town where his receptionist lives and entertains ... him. Her salary, as a receptionist, is deductible.

There are other stories, equally rich in human stupidity. I'm reminded of Herman Springer, an exceedingly prominent gynecologist, so renowned that a frequently used smear test is known as the Springer smear. Although he practiced in several reputable Chicago hospitals, Herman was caught a year ago performing an abortion in his office for $400. His patient was a Protestant married to a Catholic. In her forties and pregnant again, she had sought Herman's assistance without her husband's knowledge. The husband had grown suspicious, followed her and called the cops. Poor Herman. He pleaded guilty, drew a six-month suspended sentence, lost his license and sank into obscure retirement. Most of his colleagues have no idea what's happened to Herman. But I think of him everytime I do a Springer smear.

Why didn't he take the easy way out and do it in a hospital? We'll never know. It's one of those stories from life that again prove truth is infinitely stranger and more illogical than fiction. If pressed, I would say that Herman was suffering not so much from an acute need for cash as from the unbearable itch to play God.

This is yet another pressure which makes doctors perform abortions.

Apparently it isn't enough for them to help a woman give birth to a child and share in that creative act. Apparently it doesn't fully satisfy them to save lives, either. Obviously there are some doctors who can only experience utter fulfillment by actually electing to play with the fear, guilt, tension and chaos of another person's life, someone helpless, delivered all trussed like a chicken by the inevitable bonds of pregnancy.

I can picture Herman now, seated behind his rather large mahogany desk on a somewhat ratty black leather chair, with the distraught Protestant wife telling her sad story before him. I can see Herman nodding sagely, savoring the sense of trapped-ness that this woman exudes. The odor of fear is perfume to Herman. The stricken look in the woman's eyes pierces him with a thrilling sense of power.

"Um, I see." Pause. "Yes, quite a bad spot to be in." Pause. "Very little anyone can do." Longer pause.

If God is a sadist, then Herman was playing God . . . again.

I should note, in passing, that the kind of abortions I have been discussing are those performed during the first two months of pregnancy, when it is still relatively easy to remove the embryo by a simple D-and-C technique. Many times the patient isn't even pregnant and the "abortion" is a fake. With the development of a fetus proceeding at an accelerated pace, it not only becomes more difficult to abort a pregnancy, it also becomes much harder to pass it off as a simple curettage in the same reputable hospital where the same reputable doctor performed so many D-and-C abortions. Now there is too much tissue to be removed. Now the strain on the mother grows increasingly harder and the operation increasingly riskier. The costs also go up to match the risk. And the cover-up techniques become increasingly more difficult.

There are very few excuses for performing what will instantly be seen, if only from a gross examination of the removed tissue, as a mid-trimester abortion. Hardly any are really strong enough to justify the operation. Doctors can try to claim that the life of the mother is in danger. They can invent an earlier bout with German measles which has undoubtedly produced a congenital anomaly, a monster which cannot be allowed to grow to full term. They can in some places secure help from psychiatric colleagues who may be able to claim that the mother is psychotic and should not bear a child.

None of these excuses works everywhere. Committees spot them quickly. But they are constantly tried and they often succeed if they carry with them the strong assurance of a respected OB-GYN man whose word is unquestioned in the hospital where he works.

Actually, through a recently developed technique, the mid-trimester abortion has become much simpler to perform and virtually impossible to detect. A strong saline solution is injected with a hypodermic needle through the abdominal and uterine wall directly into the amniotic sac, replacing fluid previously withdrawn. It so changes the character of the fluid as to kill the fetus, force the uterus to give up its own water and, in the process, start premature labor contractions. Abortion results in short order and, depending on how completely the uterus empties, little more need be done by the doctor except perhaps a D-and-C. The affair is listed as a spontaneous abortion.

The saline-injection abortion may yet give a new lease on life to the woman who decides too late to have a "standard" abortion. It represents, for the too-late patient, the same degree of safeness and security that the D-and-C represents to the lady who applies in time. "Too late" may eventually become a misnomer in this field. It may never be too late, always providing there is a doctor on hand with the proper techniques and a patient with the proper amount of cash.

As for the woman who can't afford a proper abortion at any time during her pregnancy, the new technique is just another of those shimmering facets of the American Dream—like the way people live in TV comedy shows—which she may know about but will never experience.

For her the American Dream becomes a reality in some back alley where for $5 a dirty stranger infects or injures her womb and she finishes the adventure in the welfare ward, near death.

Which, at that point, she may welcome.

Prejudice

I must tell you about Melchior Diosdado Ortega, M.D., late of Ponce, Puerto Rico, currently of Upper Manhattan.

But to do so without an explanation would open me to hot accusations of prejudice. The whole question of ethnic and religious minorities in medicine—the place of the Negro and Puerto Rican people in today's scene, and of the Jews, Italians and Irish in an earlier era—is as complex and puzzling as life itself. Its complexity is legitimate, since the problem of prejudice in medicine is identical with the problem of prejudice in the rest of life as it is led in our society.

Let's begin by stating the obvious. Every medical school in the country has a quota system—admitted or secret—which limits the number of students it will take from certain backgrounds.

I say every medical school. I mean from the best and most respected to the least-qualified and most corrupt. And I mean that these schools have quotas which exclude all but a certain number of Jews, Negroes and Puerto Ricans. This is true of all medical schools. Some, of course, also maintain additional quotas on various other racial, ethnic, national and religious groups.

If one talks to the dean of admissions of a medical school in a man-to-man, even a doctor-to-doctor, fashion, pointing out that since the nation desperately needs more doctors, the quota system should be dropped, he will usually answer you in one of the following ways:

"As it is right now, the percentage of Jews [Negroes, Puerto Ricans] to other students here is higher than it is in the general population. Don't tell me we're prejudiced. We're training more than they merit on a per-capita basis."

Or: "We can't train more Puerto Ricans [Negroes, Jews] than the patient population will accept. Sure, maybe Puerto Rican neighborhoods are short of doctors, but it would be really vicious segregation if we trained a student on the assumption he would be shoved right back in the ghetto he came from to practice medicine."

Or: "We'd love to admit more Negroes [Puerto Ricans], but how many can afford the tuition and how many can make the grade academically? I'm not saying they aren't innately as bright as any other groups. But from the cradle on up, they've been systematically undereducated and impoverished."

Of all the reasons, truthful and otherwise, perhaps the last begins to make the most sense. For it is certainly true that the part minorities are forced to play in medicine cannot be blamed on medical schools or hospitals. Our dean is right about that . . . it starts in the cradle.

But there are far more complications than simple questions of who shall enter medical school and who shall not. Let's examine a few.

Let's look at the "In" basket of the doctor who is in charge of recruiting interns at a respected voluntary or public hospital. If the hospital is a good one, this basket is filled with applications from virtually every medical school in the country. They arrive together with transcripts of credits, including grades earned and in many cases faculty evaluations.

Let's suppose the doctor has to find 30 new interns. He weeds them out of the pile of many hundreds of applicants by checking their grades and the evaluations of their teachers. Since he desperately needs 30 good men, let's suppose he pays no attention whatsoever to ethnic, religious, national or racial background. This is a fair supposition but, as we will see later, a naïve one. At any rate, let's suppose he makes his selection solely on the basis of academic achievement. How many of the 30 that he picks will be Negroes or Puerto Ricans?

The odds are against there being as many representatives of these two minorities as their percentage in the general population warrants. For example, Negroes make up about 10 percent of the U.S. population. There will definitely not be three Negro interns among the 30 selected.

Many factors produce this imbalance. One, as we have seen, is the quota system which restricts the entrance of Negroes to medical school. Another factor is the nature of the young Negro who does get into medical school.

It is perfectly possible that among those admitted there will be one especially gifted Negro student whose high school and undergraduate college grades are at the top of his class. Much more likely, however, in view of the tremendous cost of a medical education, is that the Negro admitted to medical school is the son or daughter of well-to-do parents. This means that, like most of his white classmates, he will end up in the huge middle chunk of the class curve, neither terribly brilliant nor terribly stupid. In plain words, for a Negro to be admitted to medical school says more about his ability to pay than his ability to make top grades.

Let's go back to the doctor and his "In" basket. He checks his 30 finalists, all chosen by academic achievement. Being a liberal, he is shocked not to find three Negroes, or even one. In most cases he finds none at all.

But this can't be allowed to happen. If only for the appearance of the thing, this class of interns must have one token Negro. So the doctor delves back into the applications on a purely racial basis. He does exactly what many state laws forbid him to do: he selects on the basis of race. He finds a Negro applicant and admits him, bumping a more highly qualified white applicant off the list to make room.

Now we reach the next level of complication in this whole complex matter of prejudice in medicine.

We have seen that while in one part of the medical world there are quotas discriminating against minorities, in another part there may be reverse quotas by which minorities are favored at the expense of others.

Now let's follow this entering intern group of 29 whites and one Negro as they filter into the life stream of the hospital, treat patients, work up histories, assist residents and in general learn more about medicine.

For the first time, now, they are dealing with patients. Negro male interns are handling white female patients. Negro female interns—rare, indeed—are handling white male patients. This, of course, simply doesn't happen in a Southern hospital. Up North a great many white female patients will complain. A few white male patients will make themselves obnoxious to Negro female interns.

There is nothing special in the patient-doctor relationship that makes for an abrupt about-face in behavior pattern, at least not where race is concerned.

Is this situation something for the administration of the hospital to take command of and, in some mysterious way, cure? Or is it another reflection within the hospital room of the society outside the window?

In tracing a few of the complexities of prejudice, we now reach the resident-doctor level. You will recall that the economic pressures on a young doctor to go into practice immediately after he has finished interning are especially fierce when there has been a hard struggle to finance his medical education and long-standing debts of some size remain unpaid. These pressures are particularly strong on doctors who belong to traditionally low-income minority groups. Yet a few do go on into specialty training.

Other complications arise now that the minority-group doctor is taking on the major responsibilities of a resident.

These problems will haunt him to the conclusion of his residency and will carry over into private practice. Chief among them is the unwillingness of many patients—even those who belong to the doctor's own minority group—to use his services. If they're paying for service, they want the best and they equate the best schooling, the broadest experience and the finest training with white doctors.

Are they right? Admittedly there is a grain of truth to the idea that members of certain minority groups—notably Negroes—live lives of such second-class status that the depth and excellence of their academic training does not always compare favorably with that of a white man of equal innate intelligence. But there is another side to the question. For a Negro to have reached the heights of a residency or of private practice in a specialty, he must be either one of two things: exceedingly good or exceedingly well financed. Thus, the odds are about 50-50 that a Negro specialist may be better than his opposite white number. These are odds on which not many patients of either color care to place money.

So far we've looked at the complexities of prejudice from the viewpoint of the school, the hospital and the patient. Now let's see it from where the doctor stands. In that way, circuitously, we will end up where I wanted to begin, with Melchior Diosdado Ortega, M.D.

In every era of American history where waves of immigrants have flooded our shores, struck roots and become part of the nation's life, there has always been a tension between those who for one reason or another were able to win an education and those who remained at more or less the same level as when they or their fathers arrived. It is unfortunately true, not only of the foreign-born, that while education goes straight to the head, in some it has only an inflationary effect.

This tension or antagonism between members of the same minority group, based on the degree to which one has become educated and the other has stayed behind, is as true today of

Negroes and Puerto Ricans, as it was at the turn of the century of the Jews and Italians on New York's lower East Side, or of the Germans and Poles of Chicago. This aspect of society, too, is reflected in medicine.

Members of minority groups who study medicine occasionally tend to take on a faintly messianic quality with little of the self-abnegation or sacrifice we associate with the classic messiah type. "I'm here to help these poor folk. I'm here to lift them up out of the ignorance in which they wallow."

In Ponce, P.R., the young Melchior Diosdado Ortega undoubtedly thought such thoughts. The possessor of a quick, good mind, Ortega early attracted the attention of his teachers and the principal of his elementary school. He was pushed along to better things. Somehow, money was found for his family so that they would not miss too cruelly the loss of a son's working power when the crops were ready for harvesting.

Somehow, interested people found money to pay for young Mel Ortega's clothing during his high school years. They paid for his books and his dormitory room when he won a scholarship to the University.

Somehow the people of Puerto Rico who knew how desperately the island needed brilliant young men found the money to help one such youth find his way. Ortega chose medicine and his many sponsors and friends heartily approved the choice. Puerto Rico needed doctors badly; its doctor-to-patient ratio was, and is, the lowest of any state, territory, or possession.

Eventually, Mel Ortega justified the hopes and sacrifices of these friends. He completed his undergraduate work and was ready for medical school. Such a student deserved only the best. Money was found to pay for it. Ortega entered one of the best medical schools in the U.S., located in Chicago. There, when he chose OB-GYN as his specialty, his path crossed mine.

I found Mel to be a thorough, though somewhat obsessed,

student. Knowing the little I did of his background and, more particularly, of the tremendous problems of prenatal and postnatal care in his native island, I felt almost privileged to be helping with his training. All of us, from his early teachers and sponsors to those of us now rounding off his medical education, were participating in an important sociological project, nothing less than a one-man "Operation Bootstrap" aimed at bettering the health of the Puerto Rican people.

At this point in his career, Mel Ortega was slim, intense and dedicated. Approaching thirty, he seemed terribly impatient with the daily routine of the medical school hospital, as if he could only barely wait for the conclusion of his residency and his return to Puerto Rico. He spoke an almost unaccented English.

On the day he finished his residency, a few of us gathered in the doctors' lounge for a farewell cup of coffee. Someone had thought to chill a bottle of champagne, which we sipped out of water glasses. Mel's face was flushed with success, as well it might be. He planned to return to San Juan and, from there, to Ponce, but he had promised some relatives he would stop over for a week in New York en route to the Caribbean.

Mel Ortega never made it back to Santurce.

I now believe he never intended to return to Puerto Rico. Perhaps I'm overly bitter about it.

The next time I happened to be in New York, three years later, attending some lectures and making the rounds at a medical school hospital, it took no longer than 24 hours for me to hear Mel's name spoken by several of the OB-GYN men with whom I was spending time. Far from having returned to the island which so desperately needed his services, whose people had sacrificed greatly to educate him, Mel Ortega had set himself up in practice among the large colony of fellow Puerto Ricans in New York and was now firmly established, in only three years' time, as the leading OB-GYN man in Spanish Harlem.

What's more, my informants told me, he was well on his way to being the richest. There were three private hospitals in Manhattan and the Bronx where Ortega conducted most of his surgery, and in these three places his name had already become famous.

"It's a new medical term," one of the doctors explained sarcastically. "They call it 'an Ortega.' It's a tubal ligation, a sterilization carried on the records as a suspension. Among the guys who live off that kind of work, it's now known as 'doing an Ortega.' You say he did his residency with you? Hmm."

Instead of telephoning Ortega, I arrived unannounced at his office on Lexington Avenue somewhere above 116th Street. The anterooms were crowded with women ranging in age from fourteen to about thirty-four. The receptionist had hardly had time to announce me on the interoffice line when Ortega came out of an examining room, hand outstretched, grinning with the kind of intense pride that lights up a man's face.

He gestured to the rooms full of waiting patients as he ushered me into his private office, neatly paneled in teak.

"You have no idea how successful I am," he said. "It's beyond the wildest dream I ever had."

"Doing what sort of work?" I asked.

"All kinds of OB-GYN. But heavy on ligations," he freely admitted.

"Masquerading as suspensions," I suggested.

His grin widened. "So these people's health insurance pays the freight, naturally."

We sat and talked. I realized I was not only not going to get anywhere with Mel Ortega, but perhaps I had no business even trying to lecture him. He knew what he was doing was right.

"These people are ignorant and dirty," he said. It was the only time his face lost its inner glow. "What I do for them is good. They should get down on their knees and thank God a man with my training takes them as patients."

You get the picture. He was past reasoning. To suggest to him that he had perverted the aspirations of his teachers, his family and all the friends who sponsored him would have gone unheard. He was listening to different music.

And what finally decided me not to lecture him was that I knew the music he heard. It was that good old American ragtime tune that every one of my students—white, brown or black, regardless of faith—listened to from the cradle.

What right had I to lecture Melchior Diosdado Ortega and demand that he sacrifice personal profit for the benefit of the underprivileged island and people that had produced him? Why, for that matter, should we require any doctor of any minority group to take any worse care of his personal fortune than the most successful white Anglo-Saxon Protestant doctor? Who were we to say that the brand of his minority status forever marked him off from the rest of his fellows greedily grubbing away in the vineyards of medical larceny? Why should a doctor, because he was a Negro, for example, remain a second-class citizen financially? Didn't he have the same right to loot his patients as any other doctor?

Perhaps there was some small grain of truth in Mel Ortega's rationalization. Perhaps he was doing his people some small good. After all, New York's Puerto Rican colony was as large as many cities back on the Island. One didn't actually have to be in Puerto Rico to serve Puerto Ricans. And it was certainly true that in a minority group of low economic status, restricted to menial jobs and in most cities played off against the Negro work force to keep salaries low, the best solution to many a woman's fertility problems was a tubal ligation, swift, neat and final.

But I can hardly believe it was for this quasi-legal operation, through which Mel Ortega's name is now a byword in the medical underground, that so many people worked so hard to place an M.D. after his name.

If there is any single thought to be gleaned from these views of prejudice and minority-group problems in medicine, it is that the problems of our society are mirrored in the medical world, often in a specially heightened way, and that none are likely to be solved in medicine before they are in society at large.

Regardless of what a doctor decides to do with his career, or for what purpose he ends up using it, the fact remains that we need more doctors and the present quota system is militating to some extent against getting them. It should not matter a whit that some patients will balk at being treated by certain minority-group doctors. It should not matter, either, that some minority-group doctors live off their own people and despise the source of their profits. Our main concern should be to produce more doctors. In the process, it may be possible to produce doctors for whom service, not profit, is a primary incentive. When we can produce such a breed, we will probably find that no one ethnic, religious or national group has a priority in selflessness. But first, let's produce the doctors.

The A.M.A.—Profile in Greed

If anything could substantiate the fact that many doctors in our country are gnawed by greed, devoid of learning and sunk to the hubcaps in corruption, the picture they paint of themselves in their own trade association would be proof enough.

If anything could accurately mirror the disgusting result of practicing medicine almost solely for profit and only secondarily as a healing science and art, it would have to be the American Medical Association.

Deliberately, consciously and very openly, the A.M.A. has patterned its philosophy and its course of action to achieve the goals deemed most important by a majority of its membership. The A.M.A. *is* today's typical entrenched doctor, with all his cupidity and fraud writ large indeed.

So many unfavorable things have been said about the American Medical Association that to point out any more of its many shortcomings seems almost like flogging a dead horse.

Except, of course, that the A.M.A. is far from dead.

To think constructively about the A.M.A. I believe one must first accept the fact that it is not a collection of the finest minds in modern medicine, nor is it in any way dedicated to advancing the frontiers of medical knowledge.

The A.M.A. is just another trade association. In common with the American Canned Citrus Packers Association and the Amalgamated Sewage Disposal Executives of North America, Inc., the A.M.A. is dedicated to preserving the status quo. It is in favor of that. It is opposed to everything else.

There is simply no point in getting angry about this state of affairs. A trade association is a trade association and we, the doctors, are as stuck with ours as are you, the patients. Some of us don't approve of the A.M.A. and don't care to belong to it. But we must belong to our local county medical societies in order to preserve our hospital affiliations and, of late, more and more local societies make membership in the A.M.A. mandatory. They even make a joint collection of dues, unfortunately.

Moreover, there is no point in getting angry about what the A.M.A. does. It is an honest trade association, in that it represents the expressed wishes of a majority of its membership. To wax wroth over its antediluvian concepts, the lies it propagates, its John Birch Society approach to change or its fierce protectiveness of the doctor's freedom to run his practice as he wishes is to chide it for merely doing a good job. The A.M.A. embodies the almost universal necessity of today's entrenched doctors to protect their diagnoses, their treatment, their surgery and their fee structure from any supervision, restraint or review. This job the A.M.A. has done and done well for many, many decades.

To that end it maintains one of the largest lobbies in Washington, D. C., and its local organizations maintain similar, less extensive lobbies in state legislatures. The objectives of A.M.A. lobbies and promotional programs are fairly uniform and simple: to oppose any change which threatens the status quo, whether it come in the form of interest on the part of the government, the unions, or a health insurance plan. It may be a proposal to train more doctors. Right now, the A.M.A. believes, we have more than enough doctors. To willfully alter the doctor-to-patient ratio is, in the A.M.A.'s view, an un-American, socialist-inspired plot.

But, as I have said, there is no point to be gained by belaboring the A.M.A. for these brontosaurus-brained positions, any more than there is for castigating its fierce opposition to Medicare. These are the positions a majority of the doctors in the country want the A.M.A. to take. Doctors who oppose the A.M.A. tend to keep mum about it for fear of reprisals by their colleagues. Doctors who support the A.M.A. may take the fashionable position of mildly condemning its reactionary position but secretly wishing it success. Any doctor who comes out openly and firmly and points out the innumerable sins of the A.M.A. and the deadly role it plays in American medicine may find himself without referrals, without a hospital affiliation and, finally, perhaps without medical work of any kind. In a profession where specialists get 99 percent of their patients through referral from other doctors, a tremendous power exists for disciplining nonconformity.

However, let's agree that the A.M.A.'s blatant sins of commission are simply typical of the general run of trade association tactics, noting only that they occasionally have a life-or-death effect on large segments of the public. Instead, let's think about the A.M.A.'s equally dangerous sins of omission, a few of which may perhaps have escaped the lay mind.

> DOCTOR: We've completed a thorough checkup, Mrs. Jones. I'm happy to say we've found absolutely no cancer. But be sure you're back here next year for another checkup.
> PATIENT: (*beaming*) Thank you, Doctor.

This pleasant little interchange, with its strong atmosphere of intense relief only barely masked by the casual language, is taking place at this very moment in virtually every city in this country. The American public knows that the first-line weapon against cancer is vigilance. The public knows that regular checkups provide the needed vigilance. But what kind of checkup has Mrs. Jones just had?

Her breasts have been palped for lumps. Her reproductive system has been checked over. She's had a Papanicolaou Smear test. When the doctor says ". . . we've found absolutely no cancer" he means, very simply, that none has been found in the areas checked.

Does Mrs. Jones have cancer of the pancreas or spleen? Lung cancer? The doctor doesn't know. Mrs. Jones hasn't paid for that thorough a checkup. Why should she? For several years now she's been having this abbreviated kind of examination and she's been hearing those blessed words, "no cancer," and she's considered the $25 very well spent, indeed.

But to be intransigent about it—and when it comes to cancer, somebody ought to be intransigent—she's spent $25 for nothing. The welcome news, "no cancer," is meaningless. The euphoric feeling of safety is a fool's paradise. And if, tragically, she actually should have a cancerous growth somewhere beyond the extremely limited area that has been examined, how cruel, how fraudulent to let her believe she's out of the shadow of death.

Another killer, heart disease, provides us much the same example, more often with men than women. Getting on in years, with a few too many pounds around the midriff, Mr. Jones has just had *his* annual checkup.

DOCTOR: This is the electrocardiagram of a teen-age boy, Mr. Jones. Your heart's as strong as it ever was.
PATIENT: (*beaming*) Thank you, Doctor.

Another pleasant interchange, and about as meaningful as the one Jones' wife had. The fact of the matter is that the electrocardiogram—EKG—is a valuable diagnostic tool for certain heart conditions but it doesn't tell the doctor very much, if anything, about the future. It's a record of heart action at that moment, not a crystal ball. And yet the American public knows that the first-line weapon against a heart attack is vigilance.

Even American industry knows the value of vigilance. A great many doctors, clinics, hospitals and medical centers sign major contracts with most of the country's larger corporations and not a few of the smaller ones to administer annual medical examinations to executives and supervisory personnel. Some of these examinations are rather thorough and include not only the common external procedures but the full gamut of EKG's, basal metabolism measurement, urine and blood tests and even proctoscopies. More often than not, however, they are as cursory as only greed and haste can make them.

If one subscribes to the often-voiced business management belief that executive talent means everything to the achievement of success, then a lot of major concerns are paying a lot of money for a lot of false reassurance. Block out of this the human element. Forget the feelings of the individual vice-president or departmental chief who believes he has really been checked for something and feels both relief at a good report and loyal gratitude to his employer for making it possible. Think only of the business aspects of the situation, of the major corporate decisions made on the basis of medical information about key personnel. Think of stock option plans, of incentive bonuses, of group insurance premiums. Think of plans for the future based on the presence and good health of certain officers. Think of the millions of dollars committed to such courses of action.

If there is a kind of fraud involved here—and obviously there is—the sheer dollar immensity of it is impressive. So is the fact that most of the expense of it is tax-deductible for the corporations involved.

The idea of eternal vigilance cannot be faulted. The closer attention regularly paid to one's health, the better able one is to cope with sudden problems. But there is a strong distinction to be made between true vigilance and a cursory once-over-lightly examination, just as there is a distinction to be made between enlightened concern about one's body and galloping hypochondria.

It seems clear enough to many doctors that the A.M.A.'s silence on these questions is a sin of omission major enough to warrant the charge that the organization has all but abdicated responsibility in this critical area. Instead of coming to grips with what, in some cases, may prove a thorny problem, and speaking out against fraud and for honest preventive procedures, the A.M.A. limits itself to reiterating the regular-checkup line like a mindless parrot. This places the weight of its reputation behind the general misconception that a regular checkup—in name only—is really the answer to cancer or heart disease or any of the other major cripplers and killers.

The A.M.A.'s silence on several other issues of some importance to the general health of the public is equally damaging. For example, constant readers of the women's magazines—both those devoted to fashion and those known as "service" publications—have been subjected over the years to a steady drumfire of propaganda on behalf of certain pet medical ideas. Women's magazines being what they are, the major concern of these medical articles is appearance and, shallowly enough, surface or cosmetic appearance.

Diets to keep one slim, treatments to keep the skin smooth and clear and hormone injections to keep one youthful— this is the somewhat shopworn stock magazine editors take from their shelves at regular intervals, dust off and serve forth in four colors.

If the diets and skin treatments and hormone injections were created by nutritionists or cosmeticians and so labeled, we could hardly quarrel with the magazines. But, by the same token, their readers would miss a certain air of authority and validity. For, unhappily enough, readers are used to seeing the by-line of a doctor attached to many of these freak diets and hormone injection plans. If he doesn't actually sign the article, then his name is used freely within the text, and liberal quotations from him set up the article's bona fides impeccably.

Do the diets and skin treatments and shots work? Are they dangerous? If we were to subject them to intense scrutiny, I'm certain we'd find many to be worthless and some to be injurious. But that is not my point. As every doctor knows, including those in executive positions with the A.M.A., each person is a separate medical entity with individual idiosyncracies, tolerances and problems. To tell millions of readers, for example, that planing off a layer of skin will successfully eliminate the scars and pockmarks of acne, is an exceedingly dangerous game. There will be patients in whom this treatment produces skin cancer. Some may suffer shock. Many will find the pockmarks reappearing. For a doctor to become associated, through the pages of a magazine, with this kind of this-is-it-girls! hoopla approach to an essentially medical matter is extremely irresponsible.

On this subject, as on many others, the A.M.A. remains silent. It sits quietly by, for example, when doctors lend their names and reputations to schemes of hormone therapy that will definitely, absolutely keep women looking youthful well into their nineties. Somewhere in this scheme there is an untested kernel of possible truth. Some women may be able to capture and hold some outward semblances of youth. Decades of research will be necessary before we know whether these special women have escaped unscathed or whether the side effects of the hormone injections have exacted another toll which only time can reveal. Yet the A.M.A. keeps its hands off.

In the wake of the recent furore over topless bathing suits and topless garments for waitresses and performers in certain public gathering places, the public was privileged to learn of some of the things doctors have been doing to the female breast. Various operations to reduce, enlarge or lift breasts have been going on for many years. The injection of supposedly inert silicone compounds into the tissues of the breast in order to swell its contours has now become a popular operation. Any doctor can, if pressed, give you half a dozen reasons why this could be a dangerous procedure. The A.M.A. could, if pressed, come up with many of the same reasons why silicone injections could prove extremely dangerous. As a responsible spokesman for American medicine, it should only need one reason to break its silence and condemn this fad and the doctors who profit from it.

We do not lack for examples of the A.M.A.'s many sins of omission. Nor is the motive a mystery. All these abuses of the public confidence, these meaningless checkups, these dubious courses of therapy, bring business into the offices of doctors across the land. It doesn't matter to the A.M.A. whether the patient is asking for a cancer checkup or a hormone injection, whatever stimulates a visit is good. Speaking against it is bad. And that is that.

There should be more, a lot more, but there won't be. For example, among the A.M.A.'s other major sins of omission is its consistent failure to police its own membership. The A.M.A. simply doesn't crack down on individual doctors for negligence, incompetence or fraud. It can be argued that no trade association ever practices any real degree of self-discipline for its industry or profession. Using this fairly cynical but realistic viewpoint, it would be naïve to expect the A.M.A. to publicize the greed, stupidity and carelessness of individual members by singling them out for disciplinary action.

And yet there is a precedent within the A.M.A.'s own organization. It maintains a special committee on mother mortality which carefully checks every case of maternal death in, or as a result of, childbirth, classifies each as "unavoidable" or "avoidable" and disciplines the doctors and institutions involved by publicizing the case within the A.M.A.'s own circles, ostensibly to help prevent future "avoidable" mortalities. If the A.M.A. can place its powerful shield over the sanctity of motherhood and in even this rudimentary manner help one segment of the public to receive better medical care, what prevents the organization from extending its protective discipline to other types of patients and, eventually, to the entire public?

While the kind of disciplinary action involved in the A.M.A.'s mother-mortality program would not deter a Burckhardt or any other hard-case thief in white, it would have a very salutary effect on younger doctors coming up in their profession. It would let them know that their own association was watching them. The tremendous deterrent potential the A.M.A. could summon is truly awesome. The fact that it does not use this power for the benefit of the general public and the honor of its own members makes this sin of omission even blacker than the rest.

The unbelievably backward record of the A.M.A. over the

past few decades in opposing virtually everything positive in medicine, the tremendous sums of money it has spent to influence legislators through lobbying and the general public through multimillion-dollar advertising campaigns, have in large measure backfired. The enactment into law of Medicare —so bitterly and ferociously fought by the A.M.A.—is perhaps our clearest sign that the A.M.A. has squandered much of its nationwide political power and is now more or less bankrupt, for the time being. It may even have convinced more of its membership that what the A.M.A. has been doing with its members' money is not what it should have been doing. But this will by no means shake a majority of the membership's faith in the A.M.A.

It may seem incredible in this day and age that the broad group of private entrepreneurs represented by this trade association pays so little lip service to the big clichés of proper public image creation. The U. S. doctor so ably represented by the A.M.A. does, indeed, hold the same dog-in-the-manger attitudes his trade association vociferously promotes. He firmly believes in the same public-be-damned philosophy his trade association projects. Whatever he looks like face to face, the A.M.A. is nothing less than his small-mindedness, greed and lack of morality, blown up to nationwide proportions.

Second Thoughts on Medicare

Everyone agrees, Medicare is a great boon. Everyone agrees it's a long overdue necessity. Everyone, as usual, isn't completely right.

To argue entirely in the abstract, any kind of national health insurance that provides payments for medical care is better than no plan at all. Any protection is better than none. Viewed thus, in a vacuum, Medicare is a good idea.

Moreover, as the demographers of our nation will tell you, Medicare doesn't arrive on the scene a moment too soon. The tremendous advances in medical science of the past two generations have lengthened the life-span of the average human being. Because people live longer, there are more old folks. Isn't it wonderful that we're finally getting around to doing something about helping them take care of their health? Yes. But.

As a result of Medicare payments, large groups of older people who were receiving care in public hospitals will now be admitted to private practice in the hands of private doctors, private hospitals and private clinics. Whether they couldn't afford private care because they were poor or because, being retired, they lived on a severely restricted income, these old people will now be able to make the great jump upward in status from public or welfare care to private medical attention.

They thus move directly from the frying pan into the fire.

In common with every age or income group before them that jumped at the chance to spurn public-health care for the status of having their own private doctor, the old people of the nation will enter the world in which, as a term, the word patient becomes almost synonymous with victim.

Stripped of its political connotations, Medicare must be viewed simply as another form of health insurance in which the individual's entire earning life is taken as a type of prepayment procedure. As health insurance, it is subject to the same kind of manipulation and fraud as any other form of health insurance. The fact that it is supervised by the government, and that its records have been computerized for speed in servicing, cannot be taken as an iron-clad guarantee against fraud. But the vast sums of money it makes available to private doctors, hospitals and clinics is a bonanza for the unscrupulous.

In one sense, therefore, Medicare does the old people of our country a great service by enlarging the scope and extending the degree of treatment they can afford. In another, equally real sense, Medicare does them a grave disservice by removing them from the honest, though callous, care received in public hospitals and other free clinics, and setting them up as targets for medical sharpshooters from coast to coast.

Although we can't yet be sure of all the pros and cons about Medicare, one thing doesn't change that much. Human nature remains pretty constant. The connivers and frauds who currently fleece private patients of their own money and stage a steady raid on the treasuries of private health insurance plans will not waver an inch when offered the opportunity to mulct patients of government-supplied money. They will have to work a little harder for it, perhaps, because there will be more forms to fill out. They will have to use more ingeniousness in dreaming up fake diagnoses and treatments to match the Medicare requirements.

But where there's a will, there's a way. And Medicare, as presently set up with its very minimal supervisory systems, provides enough potential loot to give any red-blooded American doctor the will.

Thinking About the Unthinkable

I occasionally drive through one of the prettier of Chicago's northern suburbs to visit a doctor friend. He lives not far from the lake in a beautifully wooded area reachable only by driving through some of the loveliest suburban scenery in this vast nation of lovely suburbs.

One street, which my wife and I privately refer to as Sawbones Lane, is about five blocks long, curving, heavily planted
and cool on the hottest day of summer.

Immense oaks, maples and elms arch overhead and almost
join, forming an alley of leafy greenness that curves out of
sight around a picturesque bend. The houses are equally immense, McKinley-Era dwellings, three-storied, mansarded,
porticoed, verandahed, chimneyed to the eaves and lightning-
rodded to boot.

Washed-gravel driveways that were wide enough for a
hansom cab but can barely accommodate a modern auto curve
in from the street through immaculately manicured turf, bar-
bered shrubbery and discreet signs bearing a doctor's name
and a simple "M.D." Some volunteer a modest bit more:
"Osteopathic Physician," or "Otorhinolaryngologist."

Three houses are somewhat larger than the rest. The sign
in front of one whispers "Shady Elms." Before another is the
simple "Brierwoode." The third is more brisk: "Dr. Elmsley's
Rest Home."

What goes on along Sawbones Lane is the usual mixture of
larceny and healing that characterizes most private practice
in our land. This is not what makes Sawbones Lane note-
worthy. But there is something about its determined pictur-
esqueness, as if scenic designers had laid it all out a few
moments before for a musical starring Dick Powell and Ruby
Keeler, that grates on the consciousness and forces us to think.

The juxtaposition of stage-setting and corruption under
the sheltering elms calls to mind certain basic questions of
morality with much greater force than the same corruption
elicits along gritty city streets.

Then, too, when we consider those anterooms of death
known as rest homes, questions of morality always get raised
in the roughest possible way. These leaf-shaded mansions are
merely refuse bins for the aged, the terminal case or even the

perfectly sane and healthy oldster whose family is too impatient to wait for him to die before slicing up the estate.

We don't like to think too closely about these rest homes, or the McKinley-Era consulting rooms that share Sawbones Lane with them and serve as feeder stations, because we know our chance of ending up in a rest home is as good as the next man's. Even the best of them function somewhat like play groups for retarded children. The worst—where patients are systematically underfed, undersupervised and overneglected, as thoroughly by the staff as by the sons and daughters who committed them—are something Dickens would shrink from describing for fear of being accused of melodramatic exaggeration.

Thus, various questions of morality rise up to haunt the thoughtful passerby, idly motoring along Sawbones Lane, questions not always connected with the forced incarceration of old people in profit-making concentration camps. Other questions spring up out of the rich earth that nurtures the overbranching oaks.

Let's indulge for a moment in what some of the post-H-bomb philosophers call "thinking about the unthinkable."

For example, it is now possible for us to accept the almost unbelievable, but by now documented, facts about Nazi doctors. We accept that their hideous "research" projects, involving Jewish victims, actually occurred as part of Hitler's "final solution." We may grow hot under the collar or sick to our stomach when we recall some of the revolting crimes committed by these highly trained physicians, but in the main we know the crimes were actually committed.

So, to begin our unthinkable thinking, we start by accepting this fact: graduates of some of the best and most ethical medical schools in Europe, institutions whose pedigrees go back unblemished into the Renaissance, specialists in the high arts of healing, dedicated research workers and deft clinicians alike, could and did sink to the level of S.S. sadists and

Jugend street hooligans. We accept that these highly trained healers so far rejected their long and arduous training in the healing arts as to be morally indistinguishable from the most brutal knout-wielding torturers and killers.

And all to conform to a certain ideological dynamic. True, the social pressure overwhelmingly forced some such conformity. But any highly organized society exerts its own strong pressures toward conformity, even our own. True, in Nazi Germany one conformed or one could quickly become a victim. But this is also true of every other society, even our own. Only the degree of victimization differs. The final truth of the matter lies in this: while a great many doctors conformed in this degraded manner, some did not. They turned aside. They found the strength to do this, often without bringing down official retaliation. They became less than they were. Specialists became G.P.'s to avoid participating in these crimes. And by becoming less, they became more.

Now let's jump ahead to examine another ideological dynamic, in another time and another land.

McLuhan points out that a present environment is invisible to those who inhabit it. Or, to paraphrase: whoever first discovered water, it wasn't a fish.

There is obvious truth in the idea that the daily environment through which you and I swim, tending to our routine work, quickly becomes invisible to us. Only some past environment, like that of Nazi Germany, becomes painfully clear and, even then, perhaps only in retrospect.

As we drive along charming Sawbones Lane, how difficult is it for us to consider some of the charming doctors who live and work here, what they do to their patients and the ideological dynamic to which their lives conform?

Let's explore the dynamic of our own environment as well as we poor fish ever can. There is a board game most of us have enjoyed in our youth. Even today it remains quite popular. It involves the pretended acquisition of property in the form of real estate, utilities, railroads, houses, hotels and the like. To win, one must drive one's opponents to the wall, bankrupt them and force their total business liquidation. It's a lovely game.

In my own Depression youth, this game enjoyed fierce popularity not only for its inherent appeal to acquisitiveness in a period when there was precious little acquisition being done by the average person, but also as a way of deadening by parody the terrifying fears that the era itself generated.

Perhaps your experience with the game was similar to mine. I found that there were always some players who habitually won. The throw of dice that governed their progress might go for or against them but, by the end of the game, they had won. Now that I no longer swim in that environment, it's not too difficult to recall the two types of winners.

Some cheated outright. They deliberately miscounted the throw of the dice or the number of squares in order to land in a more advantageous position. They shortchanged other players when they served as banker. They stole title-cards to property and they filched money from fellow players. A combination of some or all of this outright dishonesty gave them enough edge to win consistently.

The other type of habitual winner, however, didn't resort to such an obvious life of crime. These players simply played by the rules with utter, dedicated ferocity. No one was more persuasive in wheedling barter deals that gave them lucrative monopolies. None could match them in gauging the lack of interest of another player, or his slowness of mind, which allowed them to put over a "deal" to their advantage and his ruin. No one was more scrupulous in demanding payments of rents, more agile at figuring up the often astronomical charges on "improved" property or more flinty-hearted in demanding every penny from an impoverished opponent, back to the wall, to whom the debt spelled certain business disaster and corporate death.

Good clean fun? Definitely. Powerful teaching tool for in-
culcating a social dynamic? Without doubt.

Now apply that dynamic to the practice of medicine.

It is a much softer dynamic than the harsh dictum that Jews
are unworthy of consideration as human beings. Yet it is as
widely promulgated in ways much too subtle for Hitler. But
if one dynamic can turn a group of German doctors into
beasts, what will a bone-bred determination to make a profit
do to a group of American doctors?

For one thing, it will not repeal McLuhan's Law. None
of these doctors will see their environment for what it is. They
will neither feel nor look any different from anyone else.
Their emotions will be untouched. They will be, in effect, as
brainwashed as their patients. Few, if any, will feel any sense
of guilt. They will not believe they have done anything wrong.
They will *see nothing wrong* with healing for profit.

Moreover, those who habitually win at the game *see nothing wrong* in how they win. And, obviously, those who habitually win at the game of making a profit do it the same way
they did it as children playing a board game. I am not now
singling out doctors. Everyone who wins uses similar techniques, be it in the grocery business or the healing business.

Now, the sharp practice of a retailer who either plays the
game with utter ferocity or cheats—or does both—can cost
his customer a few extra dollars. The avid profit-making of a
manufacturer can raise the price of something a few cents a
pound. But the way a doctor practices for profit can have
results that go far beyond his patients' pocketbooks. It can
mean unnecessary agony and death. His corruption, his deceit,
his ignorance, his carelessness, his lack of preparation, his
cupidity—and above all his utter freedom to indulge any and
all of these—make profit and healing a dangerous combination
that should be kept, if possible, from forming.

In a society based on making a profit, keeping such dangerous ingredients apart is not an easy job. Nor is it made any

easier by the fact that most laymen see no need to separate profit from the practice of medicine.

I occasionally discuss with nonmedical friends the morality of the profit motive in medicine. Since I am unwilling to discuss specifics, the questions are usually considered on a highly abstract level, devoid of the blood and pain that wait just behind them. The reactions are fairly uniform:

"If you didn't have some kind of monetary reward at the end of the road, how many people could you get to squander that many years of their youth in study?"

"It's a simple matter of investment. Other professionals do the same thing. They invest their youth and get back dividends of higher earning power later in life."

"Incentive keeps people trying. In civil service, incentive's so low that standards have dropped way out of sight. If you didn't offer big money in medicine, the level of doctoring would deteriorate, too."

"What's bad about profit? Everything else in life is done to make money. Why should medicine be the exception?"

These people are neither stupid nor vicious. Neither are the doctors who heal for profit. There are no villains here. There is only a basic inability to think about the unthinkable, a basic inability to see the invisible environment. At the root of this is a pervasive ignorance of what profit has done to the practice of medicine.

Those who believe in their immortal souls—which they cannot see or touch, but which they have faith are there—refuse to entrust them except to men and women who have forsworn the making of a profit from their calling.

To what manner of person, then, should they entrust their exceedingly mortal bodies?

Magicians and Monsters

Nowadays, more than the milk is homogenized.

In the days when I was a student and, later, a resident, we seemed to suffer under a collection of eccentrics the likes of which this world will rarely see again. Today, a certain bland conformity seems to be the rule but, in those days, anyone worth his salt was a bona fide nut of one kind or another.

Take Albert Hunt.

At the time I first met him, he already enjoyed a reputation as one of the greatest surgeons in the land, and throughout the world. Only the scarcity of reliable reports from the rest of the universe kept people from proclaiming him the best surgeon in the entire solar system.

He was, indeed, a great surgeon. He was so good that other surgeons sent him cases. If he tied a hand—either hand—behind his back he could still have outperformed most of his peers. And the odd thing about Hunt was that he charged no more for his superior brand of work than a run-of-the-mill surgeon would.

"Let So-and-So get his $1,000 fees," Hunt would say to us. "I'll charge $300, $350 and be happy."

None of us understood at first why Hunt could be so cavalier about the big fees we knew he was entitled to charge. After all, he was chief of surgery. Nowadays the chief is picked for his administrative abilities. Then, the best surgeon became chief and commanded the highest fees going.

"Here's why," Hunt explained. "You charge a patient $1,000, he owns you. Every time he burps, he wants you by the bed. The hell with that crap. For $300, I check 'em for a minute or two during convalescence. After that, let 'em get lost."

What Hunt neglected to point out was that while So-and-So was collecting a fat fee once a week, Hunt was pocketing a modest fee twice a day. In the end, Hunt had the best of it, knew it and, obviously, had planned it that way; he made more money than the other surgeons and he remained totally independent of his patients, neglecting them shamefully for new and more exciting matters.

Hunt lived for the surgery itself. Anything that stole his time from the operating room—such as cranky patients—had to be eliminated. The only corrupt act to which he ever confessed was intimately related to his single-minded passion for the surgeon's art.

He would glare at us and shake a bony finger in our faces. "First one of you bastards I catch splitting a fee gets canned."

Inevitably, one of us braver than the rest would pipe up: "Did you ever split a fee . . . sir?"

Hunt would pause dramatically. He was an absolute master of this kind of pause. He would stare at his questioner over his glasses and we would all tense ourselves for a giant blast.

"Sure," he'd say in a mild voice. "I not only split fees, I used to give 'em away."

When Hunt became interested in an unusual kind of surgery, he would want to gain as much experience as possible with this type of case. Accordingly, he would let it be known that any doctor who brought him such cases would not merely share in the surgeon's fee, but could pocket all of it. As a result of these tactics, Hunt amassed tremendous experience in certain types of operations then considered very far-out. In this way, he kept several light-years ahead of his field in knowledge and proficiency. And it was by playing on the cupidity of other doctors that he managed to do it.

He was also a terrible ham. With several residents clustered around him, he would begin an extremely difficult operation which carried with it its own heavy load of suspense and tension. At a certain point, having cut his way into the problem area and laid it open, Hunt would invariably stop cold.

His audience would crane forward, almost shivering with anticipation. What would he do next? Why had he stopped? Had something gone wrong? How was he going to get out of this?

Hunt would coolly turn his back on them and the patient. He would stroll in leisurely fashion to a nearby sterile water basin and become engrossed in washing. Then he would call for a sponge or two. Slowly, with tremendous concentration, the greatest surgeon in the world would focus on the tremendous task of blotting his gloves dry.

Then, suddenly, he would whirl back to the table and finish off the operation in a blaze of glory. Besides being a great ham, Hunt was pressing home a point: once they got to the actual field of the surgery they should always pause, relax, plan their moves and then do them.

We considered Hunt a magician. He could conjure success out of the most dismal possibilities and snatch lives back almost from the brink of the grave. Now well into his eighties, Hunt is still operating. When I have a very tough case, I still send it to him.

So much for magicians. We had other types of eccentrics who didn't make quite the contribution to the human race that Hunt did. To be blunt, some of them were monsters.

Take Dr. Horgan.

He was a fairly successful "old-style" OB-GYN man. While today's younger obstetrician gets his effects through a free-and-easy style with his patients, jollying them along as if they were kid sisters or something of the sort, Horgan played the heavy father about as weightily as it was possible to perform this hackneyed role.

He even dressed for the part. The owner of a handsome head of raven hair, Horgan matched it with a magnificent moustache that looked as if it were kept in trim by Ghengis Khan's personal barber. With the discreet application of dye, Horgan managed as the years went by to maintain a faintly sinister, terribly aloof and utterly commanding presence that, when it didn't drive a patient away, would bind her helplessly to him as a bondservant for life.

As a person, Horgan wasn't too far different from the outward appearance he had established. In private life he kept his wife and only child, a daughter, on weekly cash handouts for which they had to apply in person every Monday morning. If he could have cut them to daily beggings and handouts, he would. But this was, after all, the twentieth century.

Inevitably, his daughter would take up with young men who seemed serious about marriage. At the time, Horgan and I were both attending physicians at the same hospital. While we rarely saw each other in action, we frequently spent time together in administrative situations. I learned that Horgan bitterly opposed these unseemly young men who seemed to flock to his daughter like the proverbial moths to the consuming flame. From a color photograph of the young woman in her father's wallet, I learned why young men did so. She was a knockout.

I also learned, at tiresome length, what a trial it was to have a daughter, especially a pretty one. Today's young men, it seemed, were shifty, spineless, lecherous wastrels, the end product of permissive parents and creeping socialism. Also pasteurized milk.

Finally, either Horgan let his fierce vigilance waver, or a young man appeared on the scene who demonstrated suitable grit and perseverance. Within a year, Miss Horgan married. Within another six months, she was pregnant.

The change in her father was downright dramatic. Gray showed up almost overnight in his hair. His moustache drooped at an even more oriental slant. His manner grew icier and more remote. Life seemed to sit heavily upon him. His thoughts wandered. He aged badly.

In my innocence of matters Freudian, I half expected Horgan to ask me to handle his daughter's pregnancy. It is uncommon and unwise for doctors to treat members of their own family. The tremendous emotional factors involved can affect their judgment. A third party on the case is usually listened to and obeyed. Most of us were surprised, therefore, when it became clear that Horgan was handling his daughter's prenatal care and that he apparently intended to deliver the baby.

Horgan knew how unusual this was. When questioned about it, he would evade a direct answer by hinting that the situation was merely temporary. Eventually, he wanted one to believe, another doctor would be called in.

He never was.

Horgan's daughter checked in one night in the first stages of labor, having reached the end of her term in what appeared to be normally good shape. The obstetrician listed for the delivery was Horgan.

Until that night I had tagged him as fairly run-of-the-mill, neither incompetent nor brilliant, someone you could rely on in any average situation, but somebody you might try to replace if the situation grew abnormal.

There was no way of knowing whether, on that night, the situation ever really became abnormal. I was not there and what I know of the event was relayed by a resident who was in a terribly emotional state. He said Horgan at first called the presentation a normal vertex (head first). The resident expressed the opinion that it was not a vertex but a breech, which might require manipulation or even Caesarean section. Horgan disagreed and banished him from the labor room.

The rest of my information comes from the nurse—who was afraid to say too much—but not from any anesthetist. Horgan had coached his daughter in some form of natural childbirth. Adherents of the technique try to practice it without anesthesia. Even so, an anesthetist is standing by, should his services be required. No anesthetist stood by when Horgan delivered his grandchild.

It was a breech delivery, too difficult for Horgan. The baby was born dead.

Whatever terrifying lesson Horgan had taught his daughter thereby must have sunk in. Within a year she committed suicide.

The trouble with monsters and magicians is that our reaction to them is mostly subjective. It takes many years before we can reach a true perspective on them. By that time many a magician seems a cheapjack fraud and more than one ogre looms less monstrously in retrospect.

Take Henry Blau.

Several generations of surgeons studied under Henry Blau and hated him with what seemed at the time would surely be undying animosity. Today, we remember Henry and almost, but not quite, grin.

A good enough surgeon, Henry Blau will be best remembered as one of the founders of the School of Screaming Surgery. It was he who introduced into the operating room, over the motionless form of the anesthetized patient, techniques of vituperation, tantrum and physical violence, all in the gentle name of pedagogy. If you served under Henry, your hands usually displayed a variety of new and old bruise marks ranging from red, through purple, to blue.

Henry was a hitter. He eschewed the slap with a gloved hand. If you were assisting him and you happened to put your hand somewhere he didn't particularly like, he would take whatever weapon he could find and wham you over the knuckles with it.

"Out of the way, stupid!" Henry would thunder on a mild day.

"Back off, you fool!"

"I could replace you with a complete imbecile!"

These were a few printable examples of Henry Blau's approach to pedagogy. But his words, no matter how flamingly obscene or scatological, never stung quite as much as when he hauled off and cracked you over the hand with something sharp and metallic, whatever it happened to be.

He was also a pretty fair left-handed pitcher. If anything you or another doctor or nurse did in some way angered him —or the operation wasn't progressing as he liked—Henry would pick up anything handy and slam it across the room. If it broke a window or a light, so much the better. A surgery session with Henry Blau often left you sloshing around in shards of broken glass.

Such is the nature of people that within a generation a group of surgeons came to the fore who had been trained by Henry. I was not at all amazed to see that they had been infected by the scream-and-hit virus. Their mastery of invective was never as full as their master's, and their production of richly unsanitary curses was nowhere near as ripe. But these things tend to degenerate slightly from one age to the next. Even so, they left you in no doubt that they were Henry's boys.

Paul, a friend with whom I had studied in college and medical school, is today a general practitioner rather than the surgeon he worked to become. Almost entirely, this is due to the pedagogical technique of Henry Blau.

Having finished his internship, Paul signed on as a resident in surgery and fell under Henry's command. He was treated exactly like everyone else . . . shabbily. The only difference between the rest of us and Paul was that in those days Paul had a hair-trigger temper. He stuck it out for nearly a year, enduring the shouting and insults while spending most of his nervous energy suppressing his own matching outbursts.

One day in surgery, the patient had been laid open. Henry

and Paul were working on the same side, Paul assisting. Something didn't suit Henry. We never found out what it was in this or any other instance, because Henry would never explain.

At any rate, Henry picked up an immense retractor. This is a stainless steel clamp that is used to hold back the edge of an incision, for example. In this case it weighed quite a bit. Without a moment's warning, Henry slammed the retractor down on Paul's left hand.

Instantly, as a reflex action, Paul's right hand looped around in a swinging uppercut that landed on the point of Henry's chin. Henry hit the floor.

Nursing a bruised knuckle, Paul packed his bags and left the hospital forever. Today he's a successful G.P.

And Henry is still teaching surgery.

...that I will lead my life and practice my art in uprightness and honor....

—from the Oath of
Hippocrates

The Good Guys

I recently attended ACOG's annual clinical meeting here in Chicago and met two men you ought to know about.

ACOG is the American College of Obstetricians and Gynecologists. The clinical meeting lasts almost a week and is crowded from 8 A.M. into the late evening with the presentation of formal papers, films, closed-circuit television programs, business meetings, panels, seminars, luncheon conferences, round tables, current investigative reports, receptions, symposia and dinner dances. (I quote from the official program lying before me on the desk.) Two full days of the meeting are given over to the teaching of postgraduate courses in such subjects as Hemorrhagic and Thrombo-Embolic Disorders, Fluid, Electrolyte and Acid-Base Balance and something called Problems of Family Life and Marriage, whatever that may be.

I am tempted to quote from the titles of some of the lectures, panels and papers which are presented, ranging all the way from The Suspicious Papanicolaou Smear to a subject known as Sex Education. But the formal or academic aspects of the meeting are not why I am writing this chapter.

These meetings are a feast of knowledge which help the specialist keep a grasp on his specialty. But, as in many human encounters, their most important function is to bring one into contact with other people for an orgy of reminiscence and talk. It was a distinct pleasure, therefore, when I ran across two young doctors who hadn't seen each other, or me, for more than five years.

They'd taken their residencies under me and I still remembered them as among the best of the lot, but for different reasons. Physically they resembled each other not at all. Carl Wagner was chubby and sandy-haired, while Jimmy Clarke was a skinny Black Irishman. Carl had tremendous mental retentiveness and clumsy fingers. Jimmy had great manual dexterity and only an average mind. Together they would have made one sensational OB-GYN man. Separately they didn't do too badly, either, ranking in the upper third on their academic studies and near the very top on their clinical work.

Aside from that they had one other attribute in common. They were good guys.

While Leo Durocher is supposed to have forever fixed the fate of the good guys of the world, consigning them to last place, Carl and Jimmy did not seem to have heard the Lip's dictum.

What do I mean, good guys? As their teacher, wasn't I supposed to be above making value judgments on my students' characters? Wasn't I supposed simply to grade their work and forget whether or not they were basically decent human beings?

This is, of course, an impossibility for any teacher. It is especially impossible for one who teaches aspects of medicine, since the raw material of the subject is people in trouble, sick people, injured people, frightened and in pain. Obviously the way a student doctor works with people, relates to them, thinks of them—in short, his character as a human being—is important to know. And, while we don't grade behavior, we still can't help noticing.

Jimmy and Carl had been brought up properly and somewhat similarly, even though one came from a tough section of Boston and the other from a leafy, tree-lined suburb of Minneapolis. They had manners, not showy, but serviceable. They said thank you. They said excuse me. They helped people. They paid attention and didn't fake. They weren't always completely prepared, but they never tried to con the teacher into thinking they were. They knew the phrase, "I don't know," and used it when they had to. They felt for the patients, almost too much. They had senses of humor. They worked hard. They were good guys.

I found them at one of the exhibits—I can't remember if it was "Serial Cytology and Thermogenic Responses" or a real beaut, "Fetal Anomalies Associated with Amnion Rupture"—but they had just run into each other a few minutes before I discovered them. We tore ourselves away from the fetal anomalies and made for the hotel bar.

After the usual reminiscences, I presumed upon my age and seniority to ask each of them how he'd been getting along.

Jim had gone back to Boston after completing his residency. It turned out that, after borrowing about $5,000 from a local bank—on what collateral I drew the line at inquiring—he had set himself up in practice in a busy suburb. This, you understand, had been five years ago. He'd used up the $5,000 and quite a bit more he'd borrowed from his family and his wife's. This kept the practice going for nearly two years, during which time he delivered 14 babies, did 8 D-and-C's and removed one vaginal cyst. Finally, deeper in debt than he ever imagined possible, he had moved back into Boston and gone to work in a clinic for the equivalent of about $16,000 a year. What with living expenses—he now had three children—and repayment of debt, his life style was rather like that of the impoverished patients whom he treated at the clinic.

We sat there without speaking for a few moments watching Jimmy doodle with a pencil on the paper napkin. Finally he looked up with a big grin. "I figure to be completely paid off in four years," he announced.

I asked him why his practice hadn't seemed to get off the

ground. Were there other OB-GYN men in the immediate area? Was it a community of elderly folk? Didn't he have a local hospital connection? What could it have been?

He shrugged and looked down at his long, agile fingers, hands I knew were capable of important work, much-needed work. "I didn't seem to get the referrals," he said.

"Any reason why?"

His wide mouth turned down slightly at the corners. "Politics, I guess." He gave me a big, fake grin. "It's who you know, not what or how much."

I nodded without saying anything. It would have been easy enough for me to tell him the truth about referrals, if, indeed, he didn't already know it. But I didn't feel as if I'd been put here on Earth just to convey messages like that to promising young doctors.

Instead, I turned to Carl and got a duplicate of Jimmy's fake grin. "I'm just as big a success," he informed me. "I spent three years in my hometown trying to put together a practice, without any luck. Then I moved to my wife's hometown in Minnesota. She comes from a big Swedish family. What with second cousins and nieces and the like, I'm just about beginning to break even and support myself, after five years."

Jim looked genuinely pleased. "Is that the whole secret, marrying a girl with a big family?"

Carl glanced at him, then avoided his eyes. "We don't have kids of our own," he said then. "We want 'em. But we're just getting able to afford 'em."

"That's right," Jim said dryly, "a backhanded poke in the eye for the Catholics."

We laughed and ordered another round.

Later, on the plane back to New York, I thought about Carl and Jimmy. On the face of it, Carl had at least made a start, but only on the face of it. If his primary goal in life were to make a lot of money, he wouldn't achieve it by treating relatives, not at the prices Minnesotans were used to paying, and not at the family discount. But, obviously, his goal wasn't only money. In a decade or two, by the natural process of familiarization, he would be doing as well as he wanted to on a large, low-fee practice built mostly by word-of-mouth referrals from his relatives to their friends. He was thirty-five years old now. He would be somewhere between forty-five and fifty-five when he finally achieved an honorable and comfortable income. Obviously he could have achieved it at thirty-five if he'd been prepared to sacrifice honor, always assuming someone had given him the opportunity to.

Jim's story might not end quite as tidily. He had more debts. Slogging away at clinic work for a fixed salaried income, Jim was no better off than many a wage-slave. If he'd invested his early years in another kind of training—accounting, for example—he could now have been making a good deal more than he was as a doctor. Once again, if his only goal had been a lot of money, there were better, smarter, faster ways Jim could have invested his youth. At thirty-five, he could possibly look forward to returning to private practice as soon as he was out of debt, a process somewhat analogous to returning to Las Vegas as soon as one has earned back one's previous losses. He could continue in clinic practice and get small increases in salary. Or Jim might get connected with a union-sponsored medical group and earn a bit more. But, as obviously as in Carl's case, Jim's main motive was not money. If it were, I am certain he knew how to get it. He chose not to.

Then what were they left with? Was Durocher right, after all? Did nice guys finish last?

Let me make one thing clear: honor is not so grand that it can fill an empty stomach. Where the choice is between honesty and starvation, human beings generally choose to live. It is the strongest of our animal instincts. But in the case of Carl and Jim no one is actually starving. Jim's family is in a tight spot for a few years, especially if it continues to grow, as it will. But none of his children will starve nor lack for clothing. What we have here, then, is one of those uncomfortable gray areas of which most lives are made, nothing either black or white, everything somewhere in between.

But one thing is clear. Carl and Jim are not finishing last in the league in which they have chosen to play ball. In the money league, where all the games are cutthroat Series thrillers, victory or defeat is measured in terms of net material worth. Carl and Jim have obviously chosen to play in an entirely different ball park . . . and still make a living.

For this decision a great many Minnesota mothers and children are going to be very thankful. So will a lot of not-so-proper Bostonians.

So will I.

Think about it, for a moment. Think of what it costs in plane fare, hotel charges, meals and registration fees and lost income for the average OB-GYN man to attend such an ACOG conference. The fact that these meetings are crowded affairs is heartening enough. But when they attract young men like Carl and Jim, who can ill afford the expense but are determined to attend nevertheless, then I believe we have good cause for rejoicing.

These young doctors, regardless of their material success or lack of it, are determined to remain current and knowledgeable about their specialty. I have no idea how they financed their trips. All I can tell you is that, whatever the odds against it, their presence at the meeting speaks volumes both for themselves and for what the future practice of medicine could be.

Good Medicine—A View of the Future

Occasionally, when a friend is moving away from Chicago, he'll ask me how he goes about finding a doctor in the city to which he's moving. The question is usually phrased with extreme delicacy.

"You know...a doctor I can, uh, that is, a dependable man who isn't...uh, not one of these...oh, hell, just somebody who won't...well, you know."

I know.

No one wants to insult a friend of theirs who happens to be a doctor by admitting that they don't trust doctors.

The odd thing is, few people know why they don't trust most doctors. The odder thing is, few people distrust missile controllers or nuclear physicists or bomber pilots or bio-chemists or any of the other scientists and technicians whose daily activities can snuff us all out in a few seconds. These men are far away. We assume they're good, well-trained, dependable, steady types because, after all, they wouldn't have the job otherwise, right? But the doctors are all closer. We can count the freckles on their noses. Their daily activities can snuff us out, too. But because we can touch them, we don't trust them. I often wonder how we'd feel about him if we could count the freckles on the nose of a Strategic Air Command missile officer.

However, let's return to my departing friend. What he's asking me, stripped of hemming and hawing, is this: "Where can I get reliable medical care and not be cheated?"

I always give the same advice. It hasn't failed, yet, although I can conceive of a time when it might backfire. I always suggest that my friend go to the classified telephone directory in his new home and page through the hospital section looking for what is obviously a teaching hospital with university connections. Sometimes it can be found by checking local colleges first. In any event, what he should find is one of the larger medical school-hospital combinations in the area.

I then suggest he call the hospital or school and ask for the chief of whatever service he requires. If his wife's pregnant, for example, he will obviously call the chief of obstetrics and gynecology. He may have to call several times; chiefs of service are invariably busy. When he gets to the chief he explains that a doctor in his previous home city suggested this course of action. He then asks the chief to recommend a good OB-GYN man. The chief will usually refer his caller to his secretary, who will prepare a list of three or four names and addresses. The doctors on the list will be men who work in the OB-GYN service of this teaching hospital under this chief.

None of these men, I feel fairly certain, is a saint or a miracle worker. But the odds are extremely good that all have kept up-to-date in their field, do regular hospital work, teach, attend lectures and, in general, conduct themselves in a reputable and reliable manner. Which one my friend's wife will pick is obviously based on how she reacts to the personality of the doctor. But she can be fairly sure that whoever she chooses is a pretty good man. Moreover, when she's ready for delivery, she can be fairly certain the teaching hospital to which he'll bring her is well-managed, well-equipped and well-staffed.

Why do I so freely hang such great responsibility around the neck of a chief of service I've probably never met?

My reasons cut to the core of how I feel good medicine should be practiced. The advice I give my friends reflects my own personal view of how, some day, honest and knowledgeable medicine will be practiced everywhere. For I do believe that something can be done about the kind of corruption and fraud which now infects the medical profession.

While corruption probably can never be entirely bred out of the race itself, I believe that in the practice of medicine it can be immobilized and rendered powerless.

I don't think this will happen because a few noble doctors take the lead and, by their personal sacrifice, inspire their colleagues to eschew deceit and ignorance. Nor do I see hundreds of millions of patients rising up and storming the Bastille of medical corruption.

I do see population growth so far outstripping doctor-training programs that crisis after crisis rocks the nation's medical markets and something positive, finally, is done about the way doctors are chosen and trained, who pays for the training and, ultimately, how new doctors conduct themselves in the world at large.

In order to explain how this may be able to work out to the advantage both of the general public and of the doctors themselves, let me quickly summarize and evaluate the most common ways in which medicine is currently being practiced.

The general practitioner in his own office is, of course, low man on the totem pole. Primarily, his work is in the realm of the personal. His effects are achieved through his manner and the style of his personality and some limited therapeutic treatment. By concentrating these powers on the more than 75 percent of people who come to him without any real illness, and by shunting off the remainder to specialists, he manages to perform a useful function as long as he remains honest. The closer he keeps to a local medical-teaching center, the more professional periodicals he reads, the more courses and lectures he signs up for, the better he'll perform. In the most idealistic view of medicine's future, except in remote outposts of civilization, this is about all I can see for the family G.P.

The specialist with his own office has been discussed in some detail in these pages. Once again, he is only as good as his hospital and professional affiliations and his willingness to devote time to study. As with the G.P., the closer he is to major medical centers, the better job he can perform.

Various formal and informal groups of doctors are to be found, especially in suburban areas, where they may take offices in a small one-story building which thereupon becomes a "medical center," self-styled. These groups combine G.P.'s with a variety of specialists, possibly including a radiologist and even a pediatrician. While the idea on which they are based is a sound one—a kind of supermarket "all-under-one-roof" approach to private practice—there is no reason to suppose that they are any less susceptible to corruption, especially since they streamline the channels of communication between individual doctors, making it possible for them, on the one hand, to expedite medical conferences and, on the other, to expedite collusive planning.

Another approach to the group concept is to be found in certain medical insurance plans, perhaps the best known of which are H.I.P., the Health Insurance Plan of New York and the Permanente Plan on the West Coast. Under H.I.P., a group of potential patients in one area of a city is brought together with a group of doctors of various specialties, also in roughly the same geographic area. Members of the plan must use the H.I.P. doctors to which they are assigned. But H.I.P. doctors are not restricted in their practice to serving only members of the plan.

The flaw is immediately apparent. When a doctor has both assured practice at fixed fees and private practice at unregulated fees, it is too much to expect that he will devote equal time, equal effort, equal concentration, equal thought, equal concern, to the two classes of patient. To believe he will play no favorites is to reveal a lovable ignorance of human nature. Yes, there are men who may devote themselves equally to both types of work. They are about as common as organ-playing minister-physicians in the Congo.

A popular variation on the basic group concept is found

among trade unions. The medical panel or group which serves the membership of a particular union or local thereof may operate solely in an as-required capacity, or may work full-time for a paycheck tendered by the union. Several types of union medicine plans are in current practice. The United Mine Workers, for example, and the Mine, Mill and Smelter Workers have prepaid medical plans which cover every possible eventuality. In many of the towns where such unions have a significant number of members, the union plan is often the only way anyone in the community can get medical attention. In New York and Chicago, a number of unions also provide this kind of complete coverage through their own doctors.

Basically sound, the idea of union-sponsored medicine has proven itself something of a two-edged sword. Some union plans are extremely well managed and provide excellent care. Others seem to be no more immune to corruption than private practice. Medical chiefs are appointed by union leaders on the basis of payoffs, favors returned and other political considerations. These corrupt medical chiefs then appoint doctors on the same basis, including kickbacks. Eventually, as has happened in several cases, the entire crew has had to be let go, and the medical service rebuilt from scratch—with no guarantee against the same sordid thing happening again.

Two outstanding examples of union-sponsored plans provide some insight into the problems that must be solved in this area of medicine. One plan, perhaps the best administered in the nation, achieved excellence because the union management voluntarily removed itself from direct control of the plan. Medical service is administered by a group of doctors attached to a local hospital-medical-school complex, through which all service is provided. In this way medicine is totally divorced from union politics and everyone benefits.

Another, entirely different, plan provides basic money allowances to union members, so many dollars for this ailment or that operation. In this it resembles a typical health insurance plan. The difference is this: the members can go to any doctor they wish and the union will pay up to the full allowance for whatever service is required, but the union has also concluded agreements with a large group of highly respected doctors who have agreed that they will charge no more than the fixed allowances.

In other words, use a union-sponsored doctor and all bills are paid. Use another doctor and pay whatever charges accrue beyond the basic allowance. This plan provides complete freedom of choice and maximum economic support. With an array of topnotch medical talent lined up as participating doctors, it also provides access to some of the best men in that city.

To date about 25 percent of the union's membership use the plan. The rest? There's no way of knowing why they distrust the plan. Perhaps they've been brainwashed once too often by the "socialized medicine" scare publicity. Perhaps it's simply one of those irrational streaks in human nature that seems most often to come to the surface in the doctor-patient relationship.

Somewhere between the various group-medicine approaches and the ultimate in good medicine, the medical-school hospital, lie various other possible sources of good medical care. One of these is the large voluntary hospital which has some kind of teaching facilities. Every big city has several of these and each hospital has a place for a few interns and a few residents, although the institution itself is not part of a medical school.

Its chief drawback to providing absolutely top care, however, lies in the fact that its prime responsibility is the filling of beds. Teaching is a secondary activity. Thus, its research facilities, if they exist, are nowhere as diverse or as deep-reaching as those of a medical-school hospital, nor does it have a full-time staff of such size and variety.

Even here, however, a shift is beginning to take place. The more reputable of the large voluntary hospitals have come to realize that providing good medical care requires more research and more teaching. They are affiliating with nearby medical schools on a more formal basis. They are increasing their research facilities and their full-time staff. Any hospital which takes this route will eventually end up all but indistinguishable from a medical-school hospital, which will be to everyone's benefit.

I have not meant to exclude large medical centers like the Lahey Clinic in Boston, for example, or the Crile in Cleveland from the list of places in which extremely good medical care can be gotten. Obviously these centers, with or without formal affiliation with medical schools, have the size, scope, research facilities and staff to provide their patients with reliable and knowledgeable service and still make a profit.

If pushed to the wall, however, my vote still goes to the medical-school hospital. Perhaps the quality of work is no better than at an extremely good voluntary hospital or medical center. But the chances for corruption have been reduced, almost systematically, to an absolute minimum while opportunities to serve the broadest segments of the community, from the most impoverished to the most wealthy, have been opened fully.

Let me bolster this opinion of mine by describing some of the ways in which the typical medical-school hospital operates. To begin with, every case is a teaching case, whether private or not. It's open to every intern, resident and attending physician. Anyone can consult the chart. Anyone can join on teaching rounds. One can appreciate, I believe, what kind of damper this puts on the careless, the unscrupulous and the venal.

Equally important, the medical-school hospital attracts the

best people at every level: the most promising students, the best-trained residents, the most knowledgeable attending physicians, the finest research men, the most proven administrators. This is the result of having the best equipment and facilities. It produces a result of its own: it attracts more scholarship contributions and larger research grants.

In many medical-school hospital situations, a voluntary and a public hospital are linked, administratively, to give students a broader range of experience. This has the not inconsiderable effect of providing welfare patients in the public hospital with some of the finest medical care available in their city. In one such pair of hospitals, for example, teaching is done in both institutions. Teaching rounds are made among both welfare and private patients. Lectures and seminars are held at both buildings. Teaching experiences encountered in one hospital enrich the common fund of knowledge. Research is carried on in both places.

What about the doctor in private practice who is affiliated with a medical-school hospital? He may teach, serve as an attending physician, make rounds, but still have a private practice. If the H.I.P.-type doctor cannot be expected to give equally of himself to private and plan patients, what about the doctor I have just described?

One answer to the problem—and no matter how honest his intentions, it remains a problem for even the most ethical of doctors—is for the hospital with which he is affiliated to set a limit on the amount of money he can earn in private practice, but pay fully or in part for voluntary work now done without pay.

In this way, with the combined offer of a fixed income, instant access to knowledge and the availability of research facilities, some of these hospitals have been successful in persuading a number of extremely good doctors to limit their private practice to a bare minimum. Since there are signs of similar trends at work in a few of the better voluntary hospitals where upgrading is already under way, the day may yet come when the problems created by making a profit out of healing have been reduced to a negligible level for many of our finest doctors.

If and when that day comes, the hospital with a strong teaching affiliation will serve as a fairly honest beacon for patient and doctor alike. Instead of the less than 90 such institutions now in existence, there may be 200 distributed more evenly across the country than is now the case. We will thus have started to solve two problems in one. We will be producing more doctors and we will be providing better, more honest medical care.

There will still be corruption. There will still be extensive private practice, private hospitals and private clinics where money, not healing, is the primary objective. But the more widespread availability of medical-school hospital service will bring honest medical care within the reach of more people. Eventually, if we can last that long, the comparison between one type of care and the other will become obvious to those who patronize charlatans and thieves.

Now. All we have to do is last that long.

The Shape of Things to Come

You and I have come a long way, and sometimes a sordid one, since I first related an early experience of mine as a young resident under Dr. Hagen. Now you've met me in a senior role, with two of my former residents. The cycle is almost complete. It only requires that Carl and Jim get to work training the next batch of rookies.

What will the shape of things be in the next generation of medical teaching and practice?

I have already indicated that I believe the best practice will be carried on where the best teaching is done, in medical-school hospitals. But this is by no means a sure thing, merely a probability. Teaching and practice are not qualities with a separate existence of their own. They come into being only through teachers and practitioners.

Before we know the shape of things to come, we have to get an idea of the kind of people who will bring these things to pass. One of the reasons I can view the past and present of medicine with a disgusted kind of resignation and still have hopes for the future is that I have seen some of the types of people who will bring the future into being.

You've met Jim and Carl. Now meet the man who's really responsible for young doctors like them: Bill Morgen.

Bill is the chief of his particular specialty in the voluntary hospital where he works. This means he's responsible for the entire service, the doctors in it and everything that goes on in its name. He is also a professor at the medical school attached to the hospital. He functions as director of his service in the public hospital linked with the voluntary one. He makes daily rounds in both institutions. He holds seminars, conferences and discussions. He meets with committees. He visits patients. He lectures. For several weeks a year he visits similar medical-school-hospital-clinic setups in other cities, where he makes rounds, teaches, etc. He is also the man who keeps tabs on all the research done in his hospital on his service and takes a lively interest in research done elsewhere. He attends nationwide gatherings, conferences and conventions. He solicits money from the government for research projects. He interests private industry in making other research grants. He supervises the sub-specialties his residents undertake to learn. He suggests ideas for them. He gets them research work. He works with the trustees of the hospital and the board of the medical school and the agencies and city departments on matters pertaining to the public hospital and clinic. He has a small private practice, the income from which is limited by the hospital to a certain level. He is part specialist, part teacher, part administrator, part fund-raiser, part politician, part adviser, part missionary. On the seventh day he works.

Bill Morgen, I submit, is an entirely new breed of medical chief. The shape of the things he does is the shape of the future of medicine and the main reason I feel even faintly optimistic about it.

Perhaps one can't fully appreciate how new a breed Morgen is unless one has experienced the old-style chief of a service. In the old days—by which I mean any time up into the late 1940's and early 1950's—even the best of the chiefs was something of a cross between a tyrant and a brigand.

In the best medical-school hospitals of that day the chief's income wasn't limited by anything or anybody. A chief worthy of the name could take in $100,000 a year in private fees simply because he *was* the chief. Sit on committees? Nonsense. Spend days and nights in the hospital? Not him. To the old-style chief the hospital was simply a base of operations from which he could raid the town, the last of the Robber Barons and what the Internal Revenue people didn't know wouldn't hurt them. Pay visits to hospitals in other towns? Only to work for a fee. Make rounds? Only if a V.I.P. were visiting.

Of course, the old-style chief of any merit at all was a superb clinician. He knew his specialty, whatever it was. But of administration he neither knew nor cared. If asked to counsel a resident or advise him on a research project, the old-style chief would have snapped a curt, "Sink or swim."

In those days—yesterday, for that matter—the chief could and did do some pretty outrageous things. I remember a chief of surgery whose son, also a surgeon, had been called into the Army to spend all of World War II in South Dakota looking at chest X-rays for signs of tuberculosis. When he returned home in 1945 the father took his son back into the hospital for a six-month brushup. In those six months the number of operations doubled. The chief's son was cutting three and four times a day on patients to whom even the most corrupt surgeon would have hesitated suggesting an operation.

In six months, at the expense of a lot of healthy patients who didn't need surgery, the son had recaptured his technique to the point where his father was proud of him. I suppose the son felt something for the father, but it could hardly have been pride.

In any event, take him or leave him, that was the old-style chief. At his worst an egomaniacal thief of the most corrupt kind; at his best, the old chief provided a living testimonial to the benefits of untrammeled free enterprise.

Today's reputable hospitals can't function with chiefs of the old style. They require the Bill Morgens now beginning to come into repute and authority. Now, let's understand the basic difference Bill Morgen epitomizes. I have no doubt he could quit the whole fatiguing thing tomorrow morning and quickly earn $100,000 a year in full private practice. He's that good, both clinically and in his connections with the monied world at large.

To earn that kind of money, of course, he would have to do the things the old-style chiefs used to do. As the former chief his name would command big money in its own right. But big money tends to have a life of its own, with its own demands. Eventually, big money tells even the greatest of ex-chiefs what it wants done.

Yes, but that's all part of the way of life, isn't it? It's the life style that goes with a 10-to-5 workday five days a week, a month on the Cape each summer and a month in the Caribbean every winter. Then why doesn't Bill Morgen quit his 18-hour day, his seven days a week of harassment, deadlines, decisions, demands?

Why doesn't he stop living for his patients and start living off them?

I don't know Bill well enough to answer very fully. I've had doctors wax slightly irate about Bill and end up turning to me, as an admirer of his, with a "who the hell does he think he is?" I give the best answers I can because I don't believe there should be any mysteries about men like Bill Morgen, not if he's the pattern to which new generations will be cut.

I begin by saying that medicine has been part of Bill's life since childhood. His father was a doctor. As is often the case, the son became a doctor, too. This time the chemistry was different somehow. I have no idea what kind of doctor Bill's father was, good or bad. Thus I have no way of knowing whether he inspired Bill with his courage and ability or repulsed Bill by the hypocrisy and corruption of his life.

Either way, the result has been a man—now a father himself—who has dedicated himself to service and, more importantly, who seems able to inspire a similar dedication in others. In the long run, no matter how many lives Bill Morgen saves as a doctor, his greatest achievement is the doctors he produces.

Bill is responsible for Carl and Jim. They studied under Bill and his mark was already on them when they did their residencies with me. I'm not sure how Bill does it. It may only be statistics; he may be better at weeding out bad apples in the first four years. More likely, though, he has a way of bettering bad apples and turning good ones into superb specimens. Obviously, he works by example, his own.

I wouldn't spend this much time on Bill Morgen if he were a freak occurrence in today's medical scene. Happily, he's not. As I have noted, today's reputable hospitals and medical schools cannot function properly without men like Bill Morgen as their chiefs of service. The old-style chief would be too costly in time, effort and money to their streamlined style of operation. More important, in the decades to come, only the new-style chief will be able to supervise the changing style of medical care.

For the clearest fact of all in the future of medicine, at least as I have come to see it, is that it cannot go on as it has. It must change or everyone, patient and doctor alike, will suffer irreparable damage. Men like Bill Morgen represent the shape of tomorrow's leaders, the outline of what they will have to be in order to effect the changes which must take place in medicine.

How many Bill Morgens are there? How many will be necessary? No one knows. The need for them produces them. The need will grow and therefore their number will increase. Men like Bill Morgen tend to reproduce themselves on a vast scale, inspiring students and doctors to function as they do. The image in which they create new doctors isn't the glamorous old-time one of the inspirational teacher, more entertainer than educator. It isn't the currently chic image of the doctor-tycoon, turning a megabuck as easily as he lights his cigar.

If there's glamor in the Morgen image, I fail to see it. The man offers nothing but overwork and limited pay. The carrot he holds in front of the donkey is unappetizing to most asses. And as for glamor, look elsewhere.

But for the future, look to Bill and to the men he trains in his image. Through them medicine can become what it was supposed to be—not just another way to make money, but the science and the art of healing.

*Extreme remedies are very appro-
priate for extreme diseases.*

—from Precepts
attributed to
Hippocrates

Index

Abdominal surgery, fraudulent, 147-151
Abortions, 175-186
Acne, 201
Adhesions, breaking up, 150
Aged, care for the, medicare, 204-206
  rest homes, 207-208
Alabama, doctor shortage, 54
Alaska, doctor shorage, 53
Albee, Edward, 25
Allergic reaction to penicillin, 114-116
American Boards of Obstetrics and Gynecology, 13
American College of Surgeons, 13
American College of Obstetricians and Gynecologists, 13
  annual meeting, 223-228
American Hospital Association, 46
American Medical Association (A.M.A.), infant mortality rates, 42
  preserving the status quo, 195-197
  record, 203-204
  silence on issues, 198-202
Amniotic sac fluids, 185
Amphetamine, 134
Anesthetists, 217-218
Antibiotics, 152

APC (aspirin, phenacetin-caffeine), 134
Appendicitis operation, unnecessary, 160-162
Arkansas, doctor shortage, 54
Athletes' doctor, 66-71
Autopsies, as cover-up, 104-105
  hospital requirements, 161

"Bad blood," 127-132
Barbiturates, 134
Basal metabolism measurement, 199
Birch, John, Society, 197
Blood diseases, imaginary, 127-132
Blood types, 104-105
Breast operations, cosmetic, 202

Caesarean sections, 152
California, doctor-patient ratio, 54
Cancer, checkups, 198-199
  growths, 149-151
  skin, 201
Catheters, use of, 176
Centers, medical, 231
Cervix, dilation of, 178
Chaplin, Charlie, 147
Checkups, value of, 198-199
Childbirth, Caesarean sections, 152
  discounts, 166-170
  exorbitant fees, 135-137

Childbirth (*cont.*)
fistula repair, 64-66
infant-death rates, 42, 45
mother mortality, 203
natural, 217-218
normal, 63-64
See also Pregnancy
Clinic patients, 92-93
See also Public hospitals
Colorado, doctor-patient ratio, 54
Conditioned response to sickness,
35-37
Connecticut, doctor-patient ratio,
54
Consultant doctors, 30-32
Consumer Reports, 134
Corruption in medicine, abortions,
175-186
A.M.A. silence, 203
autopsy as cover-up, 104-105
bad blood doctors, 127-132
camouflaging errors, 104-107
compared to other professions,
17
dispensaries, 117-120
endorsements by doctors, 201-
202
as an environment, 209-211
fitting diaphragms, 171
fledgling doctors, 24-25
health insurance, 75-81
kickback technique, 137-138
Medicare's potential, 205-206
minimizing, 235-237
money pressures on doctors,
182-183
prescriptions, 61
private clinics, 112-116
private hospitals, 91
profit motive, 16-18, 209-212,
236-237

rationalizations, 101-103
referral to specialists, 27-32
rural *vs* urban, 17-19
unnecessary surgery, 147-151
Crile Clinic, 235
Curettage, 178, 184
Cut-rate doctors, 133-134

D-and-C operation, 178-179, 184
Dermatologists, 121-124
Detail men, 57-58
Dexedrine, 134
Diagnosticians, 75-76
Diaphragms, 171
Dickens, Charles, 208
Diets, 200-202
Dilation of the cervix, 178
Discount doctors, 165-171
Dispensaries, doctor's, 117-120
Doctors, abortionists, 178-186
abuse of health insurances, 77-81
bad blood diagnoses, 127-132
care of their families, 216-218
census figures, 53
checkups, value of, 198-200
cut-rate, 133-134
dermatologists, 121-124
diagnosticians, 75-76
discounts, 165-171
emotional element with patients,
57-58
endorsements of products, 201-
202
finding, 229-230
honest, 224-228
internists, 108-109
laying on of hands, 59
as men of the world, 19, 25
in medical-school hospitals, 236-
237
minority groups, 186-195

Doctors (*cont.*)
Nazi, 208-209
obstetricians, 152, 224-228
pathologists, 81-88, 104-107, 155-157
resident, 165, 168, 189-190
role-playing, 67-69
self-discipline, 203
shortage, 43
substitutions for, 9-12
tomorrow's leaders, 237-242
training. *See* Schools, medical
See also, General practitioners, Interns, Specialists, Surgeons
Douches, chemical, use of, 176
Drugs, abortifacients, 177-178
basic pills, 134
commercial products, 200-202
doctor-pharmacy arrangements, 61
placebos, 59
private dispensaries, 117-120
sold by detail men, 57-58
Durocher, Leo, 216, 219

Electrocardiograms (EKG), 199
Embolus, fake, 104-105
Emergency calls, 169
Endorsements by doctors, 200-201
Endowments to medical school, 48
Environments, corrupt, 209-212
Ethnic minorities in medicine, 186-195
Examinations, by doctors, 198-199
Executive's medical checkups, 199-200

Family doctors, decline in, 58
Fees, doctors', abortions, 179-182
checking patient's affluence, 135-137
cut-rate doctors, 133-134
discounts, 165-171
general practitioners, 28
low, 166-171
repairing fistula, 65-66
small but dishonest, 117-121
specialists, 28
Fibroid surgery, 38-41
Fields, W. C., 155
Fistulas created in childbirth, 64-66
Foreign interns, 46-47
Free treatment, distrust of, 121
Freud, Sigmund, 217-218
Frost, Robert, 25

General practitioners, fees, 28
future of, 231-232
knowledge requirements, 57-59
percentage of, 56
performing abortions, 179-180
referrals to internists, 109
referrals to specialists, 27-32
training period, 23-24
German measles, 184
Government aid to medical schools, 49
Grants, medical school, 48
Gynecologists, role in abortions, 179-181

Health insurance plans, corruption, 75-81
H.I.P., 232
hospitalization frauds, 96-98
larcenous patients, 94
Medicare, 204-206
Permanente Plan, 232
prenatal care, 44
union medical plans, 233-234

Heart disease checkups, 199
H.I.P. (Health Insurance Plan), 232
Hippocratic Oath, 138
Hitler, Adolf, 208-209
Honest quacks, 9-12
Hormone injections, 201-202
Hospitals, "abortion ward," 176-177
  abuse of health insurance plans, 77-78
  advertising, 133
  affiliations with medical schools, 46
  autopsy requirements, 161
  chiefs of services, 238-242
  clinic patients, 92-93
  fund-raising campaigns, 154
  harboring corrupt doctors, 153-154
  limits on doctor's private practice, 236-237
  medical-school, 230, 235-237
  need for doctors, 46-47
  patient's pride, 92-93
  public vs private, 44-46
  teaching, 230, 234-237
  Tissue Committee, 85-88
  types of, 91
  voluntary, 91-92, 181, 234-235
  See also Private hospitals; Public hospitals
Hysterectomies, due to fistulas, 64
  normal, 99-100
  pathologists' reports, 84-85

Idaho, doctor shortage, 54
Impersonality in medicine, 58
Infant mortality, 42-49
Insurance, health, see Health Insurance

Internists, 108-109
Interns, change in position of, 146
  choosing, 187-188
  foreign, 46-47
  need for, 46
  Negroes, 189
  as substitutes for surgeons, 67
Itinerant pharmacists, 14-15

Kentucky, doctor shortage, 54
Knowledge, medical, increase in, 57-59
  volume of, 24

Lahey Clinic, 235
"Laying on" of hands, as cure, 58-59
Life-span, human, 205
Ligation surgery, 79-81, 193-194
Lobby, A.M.A., 197
Locating reliable doctors, 228-230

Magazine articles, on health, 200-201
Magic in the doctor's art, 59
Malthus' theory, 49
Maryland, doctor-patient ratio, 54
Massachusetts, doctor-patient ratio, 54
McLuhan, Marshall, 209
Measles, German, 184
Medical centers, 232
Medical schools, see Schools, medical
Medical societies, local, 196
Medicare, evaluated, 204-206
  opposed by A.M.A., 197
Medicines, see Drugs
Menstruation cramps, 159-161
Midtrimester abortion, 185

Mine, Mill and Smelter Workers medical plan, 233
Minority groups in medicine, 185-196
Miscarriage, 178-179, 181
Mississippi, doctor shortage, 54
Modern Times, 147
Monkeys, self-aborting, 175
Mononucleosis, 109
Mother mortality, in childbirth, 203

National health insurance, 204-206
National Institutes of Health grants, 48
Natural childbirth, 217-218
Nazi doctors, 208-209
Negroes in medicine, 186-190
New Mexico, doctor shortage, 54
New York State, doctor-patient ratio, 54
Non-paying medical posts, 13-14
North Dakota, doctor shortage, 54
"Nothing operations," 79-81

Obstetricians, Caesarean sections, 152
honest, 224-228
Operations, *see* Surgery
Oregon, doctor-patient ratio, 54
Over-population, 49

Papanicolaou Smear test, 198
Pathologists, corrupt, 104-107
fraudulent reports, 155-157
importance of, 81-88
Penicillin, reaction to, 114-115
Pennsylvania, doctor-patient ratio, 54
Peritonitis, 161

Permanente Plan, 232
Physiotherapy clinics, 61-62
Placebo, success of, 59
Pockmarks, 201
Polyps, 179
Poor people, and private hospitals, 92-94
Population growth and doctor shortage, 43
Pregnancy, abortions, 175-186
frequency of complications, 43-44
miscarriage, 178-179
prenatal visits, 170
private *vs.* public hospitals, 44-46
See also Childbirth
Prejudice, in medicine, 186-195
Prenatal care. *See* Pregnancy
Prescriptions, phony, 117-120
Pride, patients', 92-93
Private hospitals, breeding corruption, 91
care of problem cases, 44-46
emergencies, 98
Medicare's impact on, 205-206
no-tissue-removed operations, 87-88
as nursing homes, 96-98
patrons, 92-94
public hospitals *vs.*, 44-46
routine abuses, 101-102
salaries, 106
Proctoscopies, 199
Profit motive in medicine, importance of, 16-18
in medical-school hospitals, 236-237
morality of, 209-212
Prolapsed wombs, 84
Prostigmine, 177

Public hospitals, distrust of, 120-121
Medicare's influence, 205-206
pathology reports, 86-88
private hospitals *vs.*, 44-46
Puerto Ricans, in medical school, 186-188
Puerto Rico, doctor shortage, 53, 191

Quacks, honest, 9-12
Quotas, medical school, 186

Recovery without treatment, 35-37
Referral to specialists, 27-32
Religious minorities in medicine, 186-195
Research, medical, drug house publications, 57-58
grants, 48
in hospitals, 235
incentives to do, 25
medical-school hospitals, 235-236
Resident doctors, from minority groups, 189-190
working conditions, 165, 168
Rest homes, 207-208
Rhode Island, doctor-patient ratio, 54

Saline-injection abortion, 185
Scholarships, medical school, 48
Schools, medical, affiliations with hospitals, 46
costs to school per students, 48-49
doctor shortage, 43
endowments, 48

government aid to, 49
G.P. training period, 23-25
and hospital combinations, 229-230, 235-237
qualified, 46
quotas, 186-188
tuition costs, 47-48
at voluntary hospitals, 234-235
Shortage, doctor, A.M.A. position, 197
census figures, 53-55
foreign interns, 46-47
geographic, 26
in hospitals, 46-47
at medical schools, 46
need for government aid, 49
population growth, 43
Silicone compounds, 202
Skin cancer, 201
Skin diseases, 121-124
Skin treatments, commercial, 201-202
Small town medical corruption, 18-19
Socialized medicine scare, 234
South Carolina, doctor shortage, 54
South Dakota, doctor shortage, 54
Specialists, abortions, 180-186
affiliations, 231-232
dermatologists, 121-124
fees, 28
getting patients, 26-27
hospital chiefs, 238-242
increase in, 57-59
referred to by G.P.'s, 27-32
second opinions, 139-141
subspecialties, 108-109
Spillane, Mickey, 25
Spontaneous abortion, 185

Sterilization, disguised operations, 79-81
legality of, 106
Substitute doctors, 9-12
Sulfa drugs, 152
Surgeons, dramatics, 67-71
general, 99
operating on family members, 216-218
principles, 37-38
rationalizations of transgressions, 101-103
sadistic impulse in, 145
superior, 213-215
vituperative, 218-220
Surgery, abdominal, phony, 147-151
on athletes, 69-70
breast, 202
brushup course, 240
fibroids, 38-41
fistula repair, 64-66
health insurance and, 78-79
hysterectomies, 64, 84-85, 99-100
pathologists' role, 81-88
"nothing operations," 79-81
no-tissue-removed, 85-88
unnecessary amount of, 37

Tipped wombs, 84
Tissue Committee, in hospitals, 85-88
Tissue removal, 83
Tube-tying surgery, 79-81
Tumors, imaginary, 139-141

Union medical plans, 233-234
United Mine Workers medical plan, 233
United Nations infant-death rate, 42
Urban vs. rural medical corruption, 17-19
Urine tests, 199

Vermont, doctor-patient ratio, 54
Vigilance, health, 198-201
Voluntary hospitals, abortions, 181
status of, 91-92
teaching facilities, 234-235

Washington, D.C., doctor-patient ratio, 54
Womb suspensions, 84
Worldliness of doctors, 19, 25
Wyoming, doctor shortage, 54